Tips for Residential HVAC Installation

By Larry Gardner
Editing and additional material by Leo A. Meyer

D1496244

IET INDOOR ENVIRONMENT TECHNICIAN'S LIBRARY

LAMA BOOKS
HVAC BOOKS
THAT WORK

LAMA Books
2381 Sleep Hollow Ave.
Hayward CA 94545-3429
888-452-6244
FAX: 510-785-1099
www.lamabooks.com

ISBN 0-88069-039-9   ISBN 978-0-88069-039-3

Photo courtesy of
SHERIDAN MECHANICAL, DENVER, CO

Indoor Environment Technician's Library

This book is part of the *Indoor Environment Technician's Library*. These are practical books that you can use for training or as your own reference. These books apply to all areas of the indoor environment industry, such as:

Heating, ventilating, and air conditioning
Energy management
Indoor air quality
Commercial and industrial sheet metal work
Residential sheet metal work
Building commissioning
Testing, adjusting, and balancing

If you are a supervisor training others, you will find that the *Indoor Environment Technician's Library* can make your training sessions easier.

Teach! The Art of Teaching Adults is another book that can make your training more successful. It gives you practical, real-world principles of teaching adults, and covers presentation skills and PowerPoint®. It presents teaching techniques in a light and easy style with touches of humor.

Leo A. Meyer

TABLE OF CONTENTS

USING DRIVE CLEATS

HANGERS AND SUPPORTS

MISC

INDEX

INTRODUCTION

I hope you find these installation tips useful. Take what you can from them to make your work easier and quicker. All of the installation tips contained in this book can be employed by one person working alone, but they can also be useful if you work with a partner.

In the earlier part of my career I worked with a partner or helper. I have also run a small business with as many as six or seven employees. But this size of a business is not very profitable. A larger business is more profitable, but the risk is greater, and you become a manager first and a craftsman second. So for most of my career I have worked alone.

Working alone has its own rewards. I work at a manageable pace—make few mistakes, do not have to redo things, and am not responsible for the mistakes of others or the quality of their work.

The solitude of working alone is not a problem for me. The ability to make decisions solo will come from confidence in your ability. This confidence will be reinforced by experience, observing the work of others in the trade, and reading and studying books on the subject.

While certainly not necessary for installing ductwork, a study of math, algebra, and basic physics is useful—especially physics. It will give you an insight as to why airflow in ducts behaves the way it does. A book by Leo A. Meyer by that very title, *Airflow in Ducts*, provides a fine introduction to the subject.

I would also like to acknowledge that by no means are all of these tips my original ideas—many of them I have acquired by observing the work of others. And to those unnamed and unknown many, I am grateful.

I have added safety tips, and Leo Meyer has added technical tips on some of these pages. For more on safety with HVAC work, you can see the book *Safety for the Indoor Environment Technician*, also published by LAMA Books.

Larry Gardner

TOOLS AND MATERIALS

Tip **1**

JOB SITE WORKBENCH

For a job site workbench I use two folding sawhorses and a 30" x 80" oak veneer hollow core door slab. Oak costs more, but it is harder than some other veneers and better withstands the many knife cuts that are made on some materials. For a longer-lasting workbench, I have used a cheaper door with plastic laminate (such as Formica) or tempered Masonite added to one side.

A door has straight edges and square corners. You can use these for the measuring base for many job site layouts and measurements. See Tip 25, "Cutting a Dogleg Offset," page 64, for an example of using the square corner of the door.

Tip 2

TOOL POUCH AND TOOLS

Although my tool belt gets a bit heavy by the end of an 8-hour day, having the right tools on my person really improves my work efficiency, and efficiency pays. Residential work is very competitive—the only way to make it pay well is to produce more work in less time. You don't have to sacrifice quality for speed. You just have to work smart.

The photo in Fig. 1 shows my tool belt. I use a framer's rig: one 2-pocket bag, one 3-pocket bag, and a single pocket bag in the back where I store my hammer, head first. These are individual bags looped onto a heavy duty leather belt. I also use suspenders to help distribute the weight. Two additional small leather bags hold 1" and $\frac{1}{2}$" zip screws. One of the small pockets on the big bag is for 3d galvanized nails.

Fig.1: My tool belt

You will carry the tools that suit you and your work, but maybe my list of tools will give you some ideas

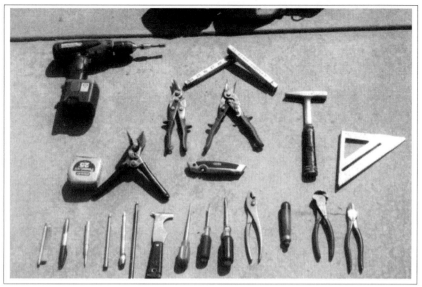

Fig. 2: Tools I carry

These are the tools I carry (Fig. 2):

- ❏ Screw gun
- ❏ 6 foot inside-reading folding rule
- ❏ Left hand aviation snips (cuts right)
- ❏ Right hand aviation snips (cuts left)
- ❏ Tinner's riveting hammer—Note: take care of your tools and they will last a long time. This hammer is 51 years old.
- ❏ Speed square (another framer's tool)
- ❏ 25 foot tape
- ❏ Tongs (handy seamer)
- ❏ Utility knife
- ❏ #2 lead pencil
- ❏ Magic marker (I use black)
- ❏ Spring-loaded center punch
- ❏ 6" × ¼" nut driver

- ❏ 6" long nut driver quick change adapter that can be chucked into the screw gun
- ❏ 10" × $\frac{1}{4}$" nut driver
- ❏ 5-in-1 tool (a painter's tool)
- ❏ Scratch awl
- ❏ Screwdriver
- ❏ Dull-bladed common screwdriver
- ❏ Common pliers
- ❏ Blue lumber crayon (keel) in a holder
- ❏ End nippers—very handy for pulling staples and nails
- ❏ Diagonal wire cutters

I also carry a few 7d box nails, a few $\frac{3}{4}$" zip screws and a fingernail clipper in the bottom of one of the bigger pockets.

Household paraffin wax is also useful on the job, so I carry a small piece in my tool pouch. Paraffin wax is not messy, and although it will get dirty in your tool pouch, that won't affect its usefulness. I use it in many ways:

- ❏ I rub it on the scissors I use for cutting pieces of silver tape—it prevents the build-up of adhesive on the blades.
- ❏ Most of the supply air plenums I use are two piece, and the transverse joint is S & drive style. Since the plenums are fairly large, the drive cleat is often 22" long. To make it slide on more easily, I rub some paraffin on the drive turns.
- ❏ This tip is more for carpenters than tinners—but a little paraffin wax on the end of a tight-fitting stud or header will allow it to be tapped into place easily.

Tip **3**

MEASURING
STICK

I have found that a permanent measuring stick is a great time saver on the job.

I made mine from a straight piece of stile stock for oak cabinets. It is $\frac{3}{4}$" x $1\frac{1}{2}$" x 90" long. I used a black magic marker to mark it all around at 5', 6', and 7'. I cut mine at 7' 6" so it would lie flat in the bed of my pick-up, but one as long as 10' would be useful. Put your name on it and label it **SAVE** so that it doesn't get cut up and used for something else.

MEASURING
ROUND DUCT LENGTHS

I use my measuring stick mostly for the final measurements on round supply air duct runs. I use full 10 foot lengths of round duct from the branch duct takeoff. Sometimes the last few feet which connect to the register boot will be flex duct. But usually it is round duct and must be cut to length. If this last piece is over 6 or 7 feet, getting a close measurement with a tape can be very awkward.

To solve this, I work with my stepladder close to the register boot hole. I butt the rigid measuring stick to the end of the last full length of duct, and make a mark on the underside of the subfloor at the stick foot mark closest to the boot. To get the additional length needed, I use my tape to measure from the boot hole to the foot mark on the subfloor. I add the two measurements, write the length on the joist, and add the proper allowances for the boot and laps to get the total measurement needed. Then I get down and cut my duct.

OTHER USES

As you use the stick, you will find many other uses for it:

- ❑ As a straight edge.

- ❑ To transfer plumb lines from the furnace up to the return air duct to align the return air drop.

- ❑ For horizontal aligning of ducts or to extend marks for cutting holes, etc.

- ❑ Since the oak stick is fairly rigid and strong, you can fasten it in place with a vise grip or clamp and use it as a temporary vertical support. With two clamps, it can also be a temporary horizontal support.

Larry's Safety Tip

THINK SAFETY

Common sense is your best tool when working with sharp sheet metal products. Stay alert and think ahead.

Consciously try to develop safe working habits. If you repeat good practices often enough, they will become second nature. For example, when I make a double cut with aviation snips—first one pair and then the other with a waste strip in the middle—I always look while I cautiously grab the waste strip to roll it out of the way. It has become a habit and I seldom get cut.

Tip 4

TEMPLATES

TEMPLATE FOR REGISTERS

In our area, we use mostly 4 x 10 floor register boots. Under windows the inside edge is placed 6" from the wall. If there is no window above the register, it is placed 4" from the wall.

To mark the hole for the register, I use a template instead of

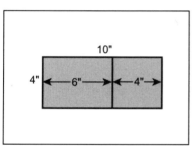

Fig. 1: Small template for registers

a ruler. My template is a 4" x 10" piece of metal with 4" and 6" marked in felt-tipped marker on both sides (Fig. 1). Use the template to mark the 4" or 6" distance from the wall (Fig. 2). Use two marks if needed to keep the template parallel to the wall, or use the straightest tool on the job, your eyeball. Set the template in place and mark around it with a carpenter's pencil (Fig. 3).

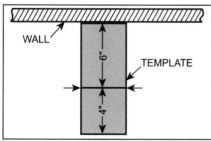

Fig. 2 Measuring 6" from wall

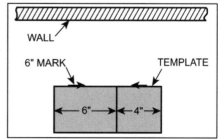

Fig. 3: Setting template to mark hole

I find this small template more useful than the more common ones with a measured hole the required distance from the wall (Fig. 4). My smaller template is less cumbersome and can be used anywhere the register will fit (because it is the size of the register). And it takes up less room in my tool box.

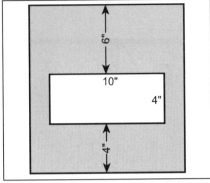

Fig. 4: This large register template is less convenient

Of course a template like this can be easily made for any register size.

Other Templates

I have templates made for all my commonly used items, such as humidifiers, humidistats, register taps (for duct), and tap sizes for return air drops. For templates that are used to mark on sheet metal, I make the templates out of magnetic sign material for hands-off holding while marking.

Larry's
Safety
Tip

SAVE YOUR HEARING

Some ductwork installation operations are noisy, and hearing protection should be worn. Hearing loss is a long-range hazard. You won't notice anything immediately, but over the years your hearing ability will gradually diminish. Poor hearing is a common problem among older sheet metal workers.

I wear hearing protection when I install large tap-ins such as for return air drops. My head is either partially inside of or very close to the tap-in as I hammer over the tabs.

Tip 5

OTHER USES FOR THE DUCT HOLE CUTTER

When the bit for my **duct hole cutter** (Fig. 1) starts cutting a little slowly or begins tearing the metal, I stop using it on duct—but I don't throw it away. I save the bit and use it in another duct hole cutter that I use for cutting holes in wood and other materials.

For example, too often my work order for duct layout will have a supply run (usually a 6" round pipe) in the adjacent joist space or even two joist spaces from where the supply air register hole has been cut by the rough-in crew. It calls for using ells down under the joist and then back up into the space where the register hole

Fig. 1: Duct hole cutter

is. This requires using at least three and many times four ells. I hate doing this because it is poor duct design. However, if the joists are standard sawn lumber, I have no other choice.

Sometimes, however, the joists are engineered **I-joists**. In the web of these joists, you can cut holes that are 6" or even larger. There are limits to the size of these holes and where the holes can be cut, so you have to adhere to **hole chart data** put out by the manufacturer.

To make this hole, I use my **duct hole cutter with a used bit**. The web of an I-joist is normally $\frac{7}{16}$" thick oriented strand board (OSB). This cuts easily with the duct hole cutter. Remember to get a copy of the hole chart data. **You can't cut the hole just anywhere.**

Because the cutter tends to load up, you will have to make several passes with the bit cutting partially through with each pass, similar to cutting with a router.

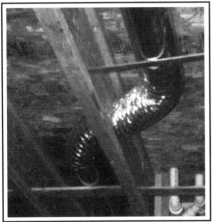

Fig. 2: Flexible duct connector running through a hole in the I joist

In Fig. 2 you can see where I cut a $6\frac{1}{4}$" hole in the web of an I joist and used a section of class 1 flexible duct connector to offset the supply air run to the adjacent joist space.

I also use the **duct hole cutter with a used bit** to cut cementitious type siding materials when installing drier vents, etc. Cut through the hard siding with the used bit (now a throwaway) and then finish with your hole saw. It will save you from destroying an expensive $4\frac{1}{2}$" hole saw.

INSTALLING DUCT

Tip 6

MEASURING AND INSTALLING THE RETURN AIR DROP

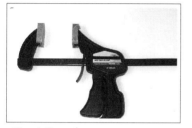

Fig. 1:Bar clamp

Fig. 2: Bar clamp holding return elbow to furnace

Fig. 3: Take measurements for connecting duct.

I use a one-hand-operated bar clamp (Fig. 1) to help me install return air drops.

After cutting the hole in the side of the furnace, I set the **return air elbow** (some call it a **boot**) in its exact location and temporarily hold it there with my bar clamp (Fig. 2). This leaves my hands free to get the measurement between the elbow and the previously installed section of return air duct (Fig. 3).

Using this measurement, I mark the final piece of drop duct and cut it to length. After removing the clamp and elbow from the furnace, I install the final drop duct (cut to length) and then the elbow. At this point the entire return air drop assembly is hanging freely by the side of the furnace. Then I clamp the elbow flange to the side of the furnace by using the furnace door frame as the base for the clamp. This holds the elbow in position, leaving my hands free to zip screw the elbow flange to the furnace.

I put a plastic cap over the sharp points of the zip screws in the blower compartment to protect the service technician's hands. Yellow wire nuts with the tops trimmed off work well for this.

On some jobs, a small plenum is installed on the furnace instead of the return air elbow. Then flex duct is run from this plenum to the return register or to the panned return duct.

DON'T GET SHOCKED

Larry's Safety Tip

Don't try to do electrical work unless you are fully qualified.

In my area, the builder's electrician furnishes and sets a temporary power pole which is then energized by the local power company. For residential jobs, there is usually one 20 amp 115 volt circuit and one 30 or 50 amp 4-wire 230/115 volt circuit. Both are GFCI (ground fault circuit interrupter) protected.

Some of the trades need to use the heavier 30 or 50 amp outlet to run their air compressors and saws. To do this they need to split the 230/115 volt circuit into two 115 volt circuits. Caution! Unless you are fully qualified yourself, have a licensed electrician make up this splitter cord for you. It can be very dangerous and even deadly if not done properly.

I was on a job once where a roofer had his splitter cord plugged into the heavy outlet at the power pole. I had my cord plugged into the 115 volt outlet. With a drill in my hand, I got up on my stepladder to drill a hole. My neck touched a steel girder beam and I got a shock. This happened because the roofer's splitter cord was improperly wired and it had energized the ground wire and the steel beam. The ground wire on my drill case provided a path back to the source at the power pole, giving me the electrical shock. I wasn't injured from the shock nor did I lose my balance and fall from the ladder, but I could have.

Tip 7

CUTTING SUPPLY AND RETURN AIR OPENINGS

While most installers in my area use a reciprocating saw to cut supply and return air openings, I think a circular saw does a faster and better job, especially if you have some carpentry experience and are familiar with a circular saw.

SUPPLY AIR OPENINGS

To cut **supply air openings**, I use a saw with the blade on the right side (called a sidewinder by framers) because I am right-handed. It works best for me when cutting supply air openings that are typically in the floor and only four to six inches from a wall.

I mark out the hole in the proper location using my register template. (Check to be sure you are not going to cut a joist.) Position the saw blade directly above the cut line closest to the wall. Tip it up on the front part of the base (platen) of the saw with the blade directly above the cut line. You will have to pivot the blade guard so the blade will make contact with the wood. (Watch where your fingers are!) Start the saw and slowly plunge the spinning blade into the cut line. Move the saw forward to finish the cut. You may have to move the saw backward if you did not begin the cut quite at the start of the line. If you move the saw backwards, move it slowly and keep tight control. It can hang up and jump out of the cut.

You will have to overcut the lines slightly for the piece to fall out because of the curve of the blade. This is not a problem in a subfloor because the finished floor will cover it. Even if you are cutting in a finished floor, it is easier to make most of the cuts with a circular saw and then finish the corners with a reciprocating saw.

RETURN AIR OPENINGS

We use the wall space for the return air. We cut the wall plate and cut a hole through the floor to reach the space between the floor joists. This joist space is panned for the return duct.

Cutting the **return air openings** with a circular saw is even easier than cutting supply air openings, because you don't have to mark the hole first. In residential work most return airs are in an interior wall, usually framed with 2 x 4 dimensional lumber. Most walls are framed with the studs on 16" centers. This makes the space between two studs about 14½". This is usually considered to be one return air opening.

To make the return air cuts, I set the saw blade to full cut depth and position the saw blade as close to the stud as is practical and at a right angle to the wall plate. I plunge the blade full depth into the 2 x 4 wall plate—a standard 7¼" circular saw will cut completely through the 2 x 4 plate and most of the ¾" subfloor below it. Then I reverse the saw and make the cut next to the other stud. This may seen awkward at first, but with some practice it will get easier. Next remove the piece of cut plate and cut the subfloor on the long dimension of the hole. I cut this line about one-half inch out from the face of the wall plate. You don't need to measure or mark a line because it will be covered by drywall and/or base molding anyway. To cut the other long dimension line you have to move to the other side of the wall.

The piece of subfloor won't fall out because the cuts are not completely to the corners, but a couple of blows with your hammer will solve that problem.

SAVING THE JOISTS

Sometimes there will be a floor joist running below the space you need for return air. I have often seen a joist notched a couple of inches deep in this situation. This is a poor practice from a structural standpoint, and a good building inspector would call for the replacement of the weakened joist.

Where a floor joist partially blocks the return air opening, I use the next stud space as well. (Leave the wall stud intact.) This gives a second opening through the floor to get the required area. Then all that you need do is use a double-wide grille (30 x 6) instead of a 14 x 6 on the wall. This way you haven't weakened the floor joist and still get the required return air space.

Leo's Tip

USE SINGLE-WALL TURNING VANES

Square throat elbows should have turning vanes to reduce dynamic loss. Double-wall turning vanes were commonly used in the past, but research shows that they are less effective than single-wall vanes. **Single-wall turning vanes** produce less dynamic loss. A single-wall turning vane should have a **trailing edge** to further reduce dynamic losses.

Tip **8**

FRAME FOR RETURN AIR GRILLES

To establish the openings for return air grilles, I use a frame made on the job from sheet metal (Fig. 1). I suspect something similar is used in all areas of the country—some structure that forces the wall hangers to cut the return air openings as they install the Sheetrock.

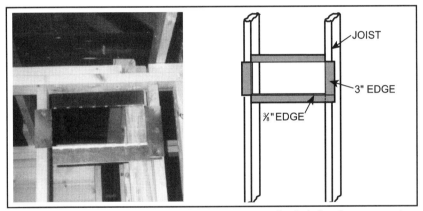

Fig.1: The frame shows where an opening must be left for the return air grille

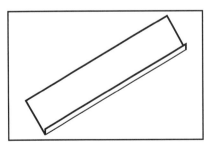

Fig. 2: Metal strip for frame

I have fashioned these frames from strips of metal 4 or 5 inches wide with $\frac{1}{2}$" or $\frac{3}{8}$" turned 90° along one edge (Fig. 2). The company I install for now sends out eight foot long pieces that are three inches wide with a button-lock lip on one edge.

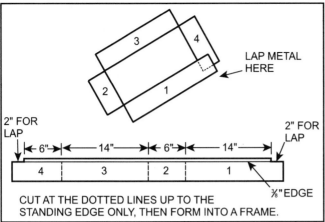

Fig. 3: Form the strip into a frame

(The button lock is not necessary, but the shop turns the ⅜" lip by running it through the male side of the button lock machine.)

If the return air opening is high on the wall, you need a four-sided frame (Fig. 3). The frame shown in Fig. 3 will nail in a standard 14" stud space. Cut the frame up to the standing edge and then form it into a frame.

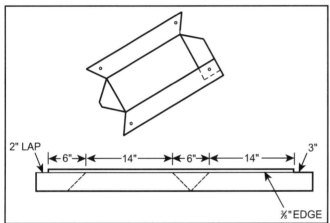

Fig. 4: Some installers make the cuts like this

Some installers make the cuts as shown in Fig. 4 so they have some material from the top and bottom pieces reaching the studs for nailing. However, I prefer to make my cuts at 90° to the standing edge as shown in Fig. 3.

If you have a wide space—for example, you need to put a 14 x 6 frame in a 24" OC stud space and the flanges won't reach the studs for nailing—you can extend the frame as

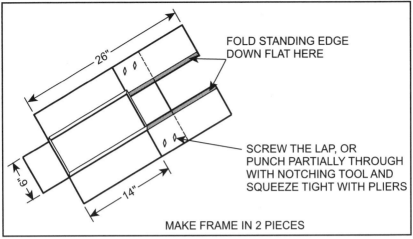

Fig. 5: Extend the frame by using flattened pieces of the metal strip

shown in Fig. 5. On the extensions, fold the standing edge flat as shown in Fig. 5

For a baseboard return air opening, a three-sided frame is required (Fig. 6).

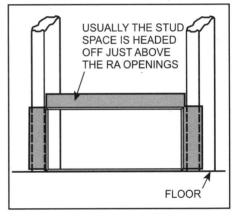

Fig. 6: Use a three-sided frame for a baseboard opening

Some shops use a plaster stop (Fig. 7) for the same application. They are also run out in strips and notched and formed on the job.

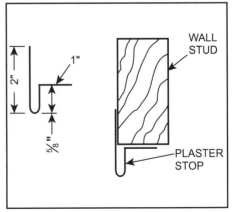

Fig. 7: Plaster stop used as the frame for an opening

Tip 9

HANGING A STARTER PLENUM OR TAKEOFF

You may be required to start a duct installation before the furnace is delivered or perhaps even before the basement floor is poured. To do this you will need to hang the plenum or starter takeoff above the furnace location rather than being able to first set the furnace and build the ductwork from it.

The first supply air fitting is usually a fairly large and unwieldy piece, but with a little planning, preparing, and jig-making, it can easily be installed solo. Over the years I have learned some methods of doing this.

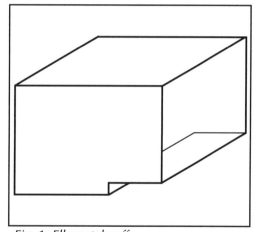

Fig. 1: Elbow takeoff

If the fitting is an **elbow takeoff** like that shown in Fig.1, and the face of the takeoff (the open end of the duct) is to be installed **at a right angle to the joists**, I proceed as follows:

❑ Nail a piece of 2 x 4 at a right angle to the joists and even with the position for the open end (face) of the takeoff (Fig. 2).

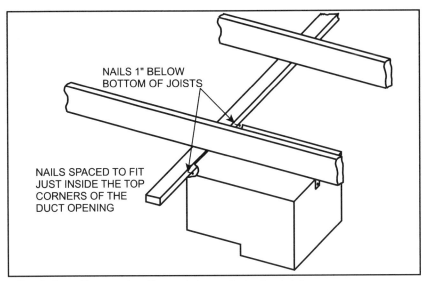

NAILS 1" BELOW
BOTTOM OF JOISTS

NAILS SPACED TO FIT
JUST INSIDE THE TOP
CORNERS OF THE
DUCT OPENING

Fig. 2: Installing a takeoff at a right angle to the joists

- ❏ Place two nails in the edge of the 2 x 4 at a distance 1" down from the bottom of the joist, at a distance apart equal to the width of the elbow takeoff (Fig. 2). (This is also where the first piece of duct will be installed.)

- ❏ There will be at least one joist somewhere above the fitting. Prepare and position one or two clips on the back of the elbow takeoff (Fig. 2) so that a zip screw can be installed through a pre-punched hole in the clip, into the center of the bottom edge of a joist. (This will keep the face of the plenum tight to the line of the 2 x 4.)

- ❏ Install hangers to hold the plenum in place.

The 2 x 4 and nails provide the proper alignment and positioning of the plenum. I think it is just as fast as having a helper hold the plenum in position while you install the hangers—and you don't have to pay the 2 x 4.

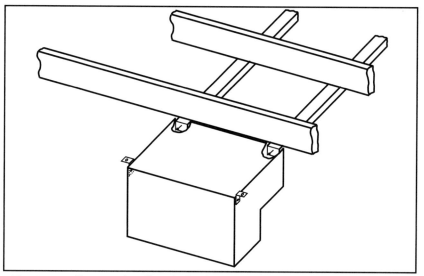

Fig. 3: Installing a takeoff with the face parallel to the joist

If the elbow is to be installed with the face of the takeoff **parallel** to the joist, use the same procedure described above, but install two 2 x 4s and nails as shown in Fig. 3. The ends of the 2 x 4s are positioned where the elbow opening is to be. Pre-measure and install the clips on the **sides** of the fitting so that they will attach to the bottom of another joist.

If the fitting is a **plenum**, a chamber with the takeoffs to be added later, I use a similar method as shown in Fig. 4:

- ❏ I nail the 2 x 4 at a right angle to the joists.

- ❏ Since there is no takeoff part on the plenum, I have to position the plenum on the nails with a different method. I drill two small holes (for nails) in the plenum on the side next to the 2 x 4. The nails must be the proper distance down so that they will position the top of the plenum approximately an inch below the joist. The nails must be far enough apart to give the plenum stability.

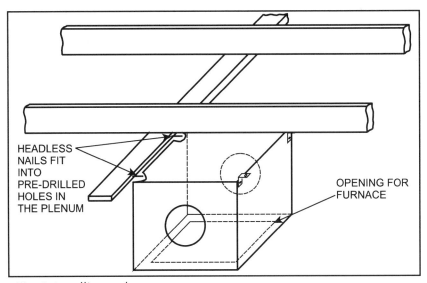

HEADLESS NAILS FIT INTO PRE-DRILLED HOLES IN THE PLENUM

OPENING FOR FURNACE

Fig. 4: Installing a plenum

❏ I cut the heads off of two 3D galvanized nails that I carry in my tool pouch and drive them into the 2 x 4 to fit the holes drilled in the plenum. When the plenum is placed on the nails through the pre-drilled holes, it should be in the proper vertical and horizontal position.

❏ As before, prepare and pre-position one or two clips on the opposite side of the plenum for zip screws into the joist. Do this before raising the plenum into position on the nails.

Tip 10 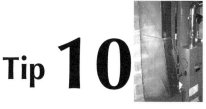 CUTTING ROUND HOLES FOR TAKEOFFS

To cut the round holes for takeoffs I use a duct hole cutter (Fig. 1). To power the hole cutter I use a 10 mm ($\frac{3}{8}$") angle drill. The angle drill gives me more control over the hole cutter than a pistol grip drill. And for those times when you've forgotten to cut a hole for a takeoff before the duct was installed, the hole cutter with an angle drill is a lifesaver. It is relatively easy to manipulate it in a standard 14" joist bay.

I also use my hole cutter to cut the openings in the top of my return air ducts—just set it to the size needed for the CFM required. Of course, you can't cut out the entire circle with the cutter because you would lose your pivot point. I stop cutting when there is approximately one inch of material left and then finish with aviation snips.

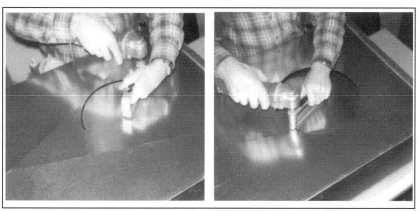

Fig. 1: Hole cutter in use

Some cutter bits seem to work differently than others. For example, some work best at a right angle to the metal, while others cut better with the point leading.

I often cut rectangular holes by first cutting a round hole with my duct cutter sized to a diameter equal to the small dimension of the rectangle (Fig. 2). Then I cut the rectangle with my snips.

If electricity is not available or is difficult to reach, use an old, heavy-duty screwdriver to start the hole (Fig. 3), and then cut it out with airplane snips.

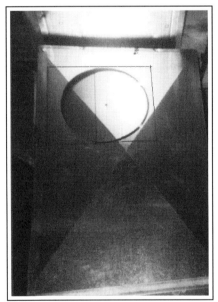

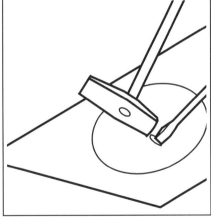

Fig. 2: You can use a hole cutter to start the opening for a rectangular hole

Fig. 3: Tap on a screwdriver to punch a hole, then use snips

Tip **11**

USING FLEXIBLE DUCT

Some areas do not permit the use of flexible duct. Other areas limit the lengths of flex duct that can be used for a run. In my area, we may use flexible air duct connectors in limited situations.

Flex duct is generally not recommended because the corrugated interior creates air turbulence which results in a relatively high resistance to airflow. Use flex duct sparingly. In general, use flex duct for short branch runs and keep turns to a minimum. For example, use it where space is limited or possibly where it might result in less pressure loss than rigid duct because of the number of fittings and turns involved for the rigid duct. Stretch the duct to the manufacturer's specifications because compressing the duct creates a rougher interior and therefore more resistance to flow.

Personally, I only use it where it is impossible or impractical to use rigid duct.

A firm I install for cuts all the first floor supply and return air openings at the rough-in stage. At this stage they install all the concealed ductwork, any attic ductwork, and the B style gas vent piping.

Later they come back and measure for the ductwork in the basement that supplies the registers on the first floor. This means that the ductwork has to fit to the holes that are already there. There is no way to relocate a register without cutting a new hole and patching the existing one.

Occasionally this results in a register hole being too close to a branch duct, leaving too little room for takeoffs, ells, or offsets in rigid duct. In a case like this, I use a short section of flexible duct.

I have also used flexible duct in a joist bay that has some plumbing pipes in the way. For example, if the work order calls for a 6" run in a joist space that has a plumbing pipe in it (Fig. 1), the

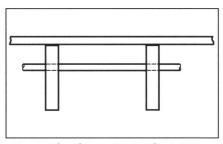

Fig. 1: Plumbing pipe in the joist space is an obstruction

measure-up supervisor will call for the use of two straight boots connected together (Fig. 2).

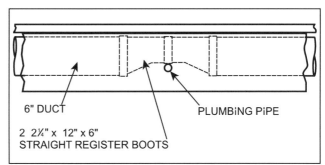

6" DUCT

2 2¼" x 12" x 6"
STRAIGHT REGISTER BOOTS

PLUMBiNG PiPE

Fig. 2: Two straight boots can be connected to bridge the plumbing pipe

However if there is at least 4" between the top of the plumbing pipe and the subfloor, I avoid the two-boot arrangement and instead use a short section of 6" flex duct. It is easy to get the flex duct above the pipe in the 4" space and back to full 6" round on both sides of the plumbing pipe. In this case the flex duct has less pressure loss than the two boots would have. And flex duct is easier and quicker to install.

Tip 12

ASSEMBLING BUTTON LOCK DUCT

Putting button lock duct together is pretty straightforward. However, it does often get beat up a little during delivery. I Straighten any serious bends before I begin assembly. I start the lock on the right side (I'm right-handed). I line up the ends properly and start the lock in the first few inches, holding the rest of the lock up with my left hand. To do this I keep my hand between the two parts of the lock. Be sure to wear a leather glove. Holding the lock up puts some tension on the mating portion as you hammer it in and helps to keep it from wrinkling. Be careful not to kink the male edge, or it will be hard to insert it in the lock.

Larry's Safety Tip

SAVE YOUR HANDS

Most sheet metal work requires dexterity, so you can't wear gloves. However, some operations should be performed with gloves on for safety's sake.

I use economy grade leather-palm gloves. I like gauntlet style cuffs because they are easy to get on and off.

I carry two pair. One pair is in my toolbox of hand tools on the floor by my temporary work bench. I use that pair mostly for putting together button-lock duct. The other pair is on the floor by the pile of round snaplock duct for un-nesting the pieces.

I always wear gloves when sorting and spreading my job-site-delivered duct and fittings.

Tip 13  STRAIGHTENING TWISTED RECTANGULAR DUCT

Sometimes purchased rectangular duct is poorly made, and when you line up the ends and hammer the button locks together, it is twisted on one end. This twist can be straightened out after the duct is hung and the hangers installed—but only if there is some play or slop in the drive cleat joints.

On much of the duct that I get, the turned edge for the drive measures only about ⅜". In fact, the slot for turning drives on most manufactured folding tools is only ⅜" deep and is so labeled. This amount of slop in the drive cleat joint is usually enough to allow a twisted piece of duct to be straightened.

However, if the twisted duct you are about to hang has a full ½" or more for the turn for the drive, you will have to trim the turn before hanging the duct.

To do this, partially open the turn with your screwdriver or other tool so that you can get the tip of your aviation snips in and trim the turn back to approximately ⅜". Be careful not to leave fish hooks to get snagged on the drive cleat. Reclose with hand tongs.

After the duct section is hung and the hangers installed, simply twist the end of the duct in the direction that will correct the twisted condition. The slop in the drive cleat joint will let the button lock joint slide along its length allowing the corners of the open end to be squared.

Leo's Tip USE A LADDER SAFELY

NO MAKESHIFTS

How many times have you used an oil drum, a bucket, a box, or a chair to step on because a ladder wasn't handy? It's pretty dumb, but we've all done it at one time or another. And most of us have gotten away with it. But I know of some broken arms and hands that resulted from it—and even a broken back. If you've done it and gotten away with it, it means you won the gamble. But think of what you bet. You bet a few minutes of time against a loss of $100,000 of income—plus suffering for you and your family.

KEEP CONTROL

The biggest danger when carrying ladders in hitting someone or something. When possible, carry a ladder vertically and against your chest. Be aware of electrical wires or other overhead obstacles. A long ladder should be carried horizontally by two workers—one on each end—so that it can be controlled at both ends. If you must carry a ladder in a horizontal position by yourself, be very aware of the position of both ends of the ladder.

DAMAGED LADDERS

We've heard it a hundred times, but we still do it. DON'T USE DAMAGED LADDERS. If the steps or rungs of a ladder are cracked, bent, or broken, get it back to the shop for replacement. The same goes for anything on a ladder that isn't working as it should. A wooden ladder should never be painted. That just covers up cracks.

Tip 14

CUTTING ROUND SNAPLOCK

I am sure that anyone who has been installing for a while has a method of cutting round snaplock duct to length. This is mine.

I work with the duct on the floor. I use leather gloves to un-nest the duct to prevent cuts.

Using a black magic marker, I mark the duct to length on each side of the seam and once half way around.

I'm right-handed, so I step on the lower seam with my left foot and pull up on the upper half of the duct with my left hand. Using a pair of straight snips, I cut at my mark and at a right angle to the seam of the duct. At the same time I lift up with my left hand to allow me to cut to the half-way mark on the duct.

Then I step to the other side of the duct and do exactly the same thing. Stop the tip of your snips right on the end of the first cut. Otherwise you will leave a sliver of metal on one piece that will invariably stick you in the hand.

If your grip isn't strong enough or the metal gage is heavy, you can start the cut through the seam with a pair of airplane snips or compound leverage bull nose snips.

I snap the duct together on my temporary work bench. It is easier to do at waist level and it saves my back and knees. I open the squashed female part of the seam with a tool and then assemble the seam from right to left. I start the seam with my left hand and squeeze it together with my right hand. Straighten any damaged parts of the seam with a screwdriver or pliers before you begin assembly. Sometimes a poorly made seam won't snap completely. A sharp rap with the flat side of my tinner's hammer always brings it together.

USE LADDERS SAFELY

Leo's Tip

USE IT RIGHT

- ❏ Don't put tools on the shelf of a stepladder. They can fall and hit someone.
- ❏ Don't stand on the top step or shelf of a stepladder.
- ❏ If you're working on a roof, have a sign on the ladder so that no one will move it.
- ❏ Tie off the rope of an extension ladder so that it can't be unlocked.

KEEP YOUR BALANCE

- ❏ Use **both hands** to climb a ladder. If you carry something in one hand, you will have **no** hand on the ladder as you move from one rung to another.
- ❏ Use a rope to hoist tools or materials up on a roof or other higher level. **Be careful so that you are not in danger of falling as you haul.**
- ❏ Always face the ladder when climbing.
- ❏ Never have more than one person on a ladder.

SHOCKING!

An electrical shock when you are on a ladder is a double whammy. There's damage from the shock, but also a good chance you will fall off the ladder. Metal ladders, which conduct electricity, are still around. Follow these rules to protect yourself:

- ❏ Never use a metal ladder near electrical equipment or electric lines.
- ❏ Keep any ladder at least 10 feet away from a building's electrical lines.
- ❏ Don't use electrical devices while on an all-metal ladder. You are set up with an excellent ground for the electrical current and the shock will probably be heavier than usual.

PANNING

Tip 15

RETURN AIR PANNING

In my area of the country (the Midwest), enclosed stud and joist spaces are used extensively as return air paths. This process of closing in the spaces is called **panning**. ACCA (Air Conditioning Contractors of America) **does not endorse** the use of panned stud and joist spaces for use as airways because of leakage problems. However, in the ACCA *Manual D, Residential Duct Systems*, they list CFM values associated with such spaces and suggest friction rate information that can be used with them.

If panning is used, it should be done carefully to minimize leakage.

To pan (close in) these spaces, I use Thermo-Pan, a foil-faced cardboard-like panning material from Thermo Manufacturing Inc[1]. The pieces are $47\frac{1}{2}$" long (nominal length is 48") and come in several widths for different joist spacing. Precut header pieces for different sizes and styles of floor joists are also available.

This material is easy to work with. I use a framing square and the 1" x 16" long blade from a combination square along with my utility knife for cutting, and a dull screwdriver for scoring the material. A screencloth tool (for rolling in the rubber strip for window screens) also works well for scoring.

[1]Thermo Manufacturing Inc, 3709 Columbus Road NE, Canton OH 44705. 888-678-3709, www.thermopan.com

Install panning by stapling it to the bottom of the floor joists. I use a reinforced silver tape to tape any butt joints.

Headers

Headers are used at the end of a return air run (Fig. 1). Precut, scored headers are available for several joist sizes and spacings. For example, for standard 2 x 10 or 2 x 12 joists on 16" centers they come as shown in Fig. 2.

On the job, many of the spaces between the joists will be slightly less than 14½". For these, I re-score using my 16" combination square blade. If the space is 14¼" wide, I re-score on one side of the header. To do this, lay the 1" wide combination square blade flush with the edge of the header and drag the edge of a dull-bladed screwdriver along the other edge (Fig. 3). If it is 14" wide or less, I re-score both sides.

Pre-cut headers are made slightly longer than the height of the joist, but this is not a problem. You simply install them between the joists but at a slant (Fig. 4). If a round pipe must pass through the header, re-score the header so that it installs

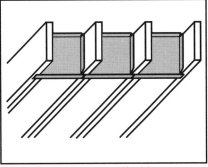
Fig. 1: Headers installed between joists

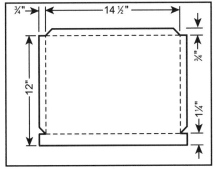
Fig. 2: Standard Thermo-pan header

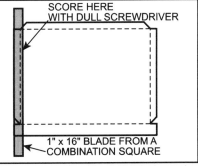
Fig. 3: Use the 1" x 16" blade and score with a dull screwdriver to make a header fit

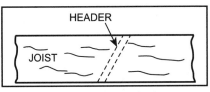
Fig. 4: Slant header to fit the space

34

vertically, not at a slant, as explained in Tip 18, "Supply and Return in the Same Space," page 39. If the header is vertical, the hole for the pipe can be round and not oval.

Pre-cut headers for I-joists (Fig. 5) are also available. Because of the shape of the joist, these headers can't just slide into place—they have to be rotated into place. Unfortunately, like the regular headers, they are made longer than the joists are high. This makes it difficult to rotate them into place. To solve this problem, I cut and re-score them to the exact height of the joist. They can then be held perpendicular to the length of the joist and rotated into place.

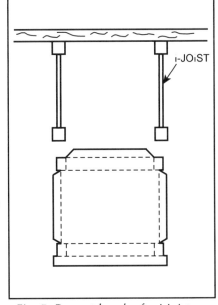

Fig. 5: Pre-cut header for I-joist

Jumping from One Joist to Another

Sometimes return air has to jump from one joist space to another. If I only have to jump from one joist space to the next, I make a **pan** from a single piece of 24" x 48" panning and staple it to the bottom of the joists (Fig. 6). The open ends of the joist spaces are sealed with headers.

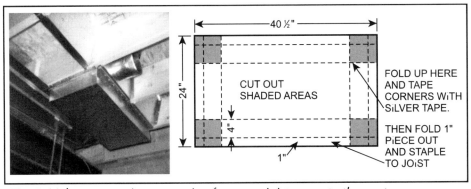

Fig. 6: Make a pan to jump panning from one joist space to the next

I use a piece of rectangular duct capped at both ends if the jump is for more than one joist space (Fig. 7). Cut openings in the top of the duct to connect to the panned spaces.

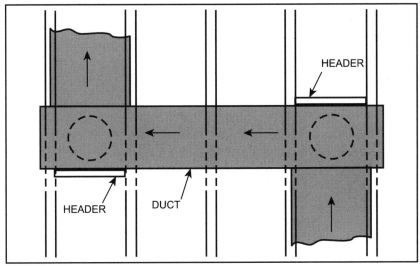

Fig. 7: Using a piece of duct to jump from one joist space to another

Install Panning before Duct

Most installers I've seen hang their return air duct and then install the panning and headers to it, usually by turning a 1" edge down on the panning and taping it to the side of the duct.

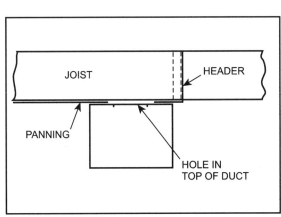

Fig. 8: Install the panning before installing duct connected to it

I prefer to install the panning and headers first and then install the duct tightly to it. I let the panning and a lip on the header lap an inch beyond the edge of where the duct will be (Fig. 8). In my opinion, doing it this way results in a neater finished job.

Tip 16

PANNING NEXT TO A WALL

Sometimes a joist space next to a wall needs to be panned.
I do this in one of three ways:

- Usually I score and turn down one inch on the edge of the panning and staple this to the side of the top plate of the wall (Fig. 1).

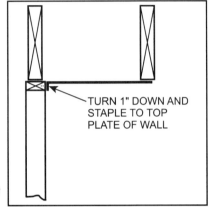

Fig. 1: Method 1—Turn down edge and staple it to wall

- If the top of the wall extends past the edge of the joist (which is often the case), drive a series of #3d galvanized nails into the joist approximately $\frac{1}{8}$" above the plane of the top plate of the wall and 4" to 5" apart. Insert the edge of the Thermo-pan into the space between the top plate and the nails and staple the other edge of the panning to the adjacent joist (Fig. 2). The #3d galvanized nails are always available in my tool pouch.

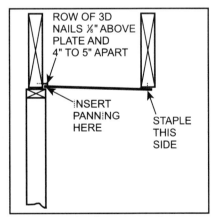

Fig. 2: Method 2—Insert the panning between the nails and the top of the wall

- A third method is to use a scrap piece of Thermo-pan instead of the nails. Score and turn out a one inch lip on a

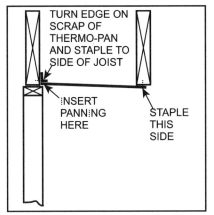

TURN EDGE ON SCRAP OF THERMO-PAN AND STAPLE TO SIDE OF JOIST

INSERT PANNING HERE

STAPLE THIS SIDE

Fig. 3: Method 3—Insert the panning between the top of the wall and the scrap of panning

length of Thermo-pan, or perhaps the scrap piece already has the $\frac{3}{4}$" scored factory edge on it. Staple the piece to the side of the joist approximately $\frac{1}{8}$" above the plane of the top plate of the wall (Fig. 3). Insert the edge of the Thermo-pan into the space between the top plate and the stapled on piece, and staple the other side to the adjacent joist. The Thermo-pan material has some memory—this will cause the turned lip to squeeze the panning against the top plate of the wall.

Leo's Tip — REPLACE DIRTY FILTERS

The paper throw-away filters found in residential furnaces and air conditioners do not improve the air quality in the home. They are there to keep dirt out of system components such as fans and coils. Dirty filters release pollutants into the ventilation air and allow dirt to build up on coils and fans. Replace dirty filters carefully so the trapped pollutants are not released into the air again:

- ❑ Stop the fan.
- ❑ Remove the new filter from the box or wrapper.
- ❑ Remove the old filter and put it into the empty box or wrapper.
- ❑ Start the fan.

Tip **17**

ANOTHER US. FO. JOB-FABRICATE. SHALLOW PA.

I have described in Tip 15 how to make a shallow pan from a single piece of 24" x 48" Thermo-pan and to use it to jump a return air from one joist space to the adjacent space.

On a recent job there were two joist spaces that I wanted to use as panned return air airways. However, both of them were completely blocked off by triple headers the framers had installed to support a load from above (Fig. 1).

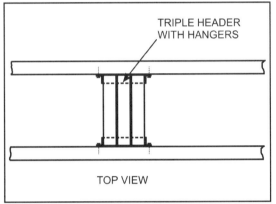

Fig. 1: Triple headers between joists

I used a job-fabricated pan to route the air under the header and was thus able to use the two spaces for return air (Fig. 2).

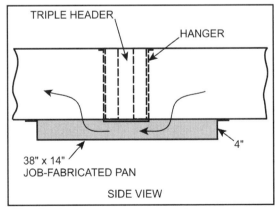

Fig. 2 : A pan reroutes return air

Tip 18  SUPPLY AND RETURN IN THE SAME SPACE

A branch supply air run is sometimes located in the same space between joists as a return air run. Where the branch takeoff joins the main supply air duct, there is a one inch space between the main supply duct and the bottom of the joist (Fig. 1). This space must be closed off in some way as part of the return air panning. I use Thermo-pan panning for these filler pieces. It can be cut with a straight edge and utility knife. (Panning is covered in Tip 15, Return Air Panning.)

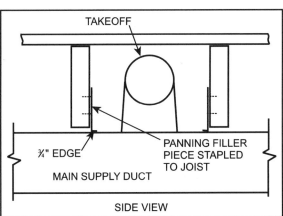

Fig. 1: Blocking the 1" space between the joists and main supply duct

I cut a piece of 16" x 48" panning to the exact width of the duct and then cut the piece in half along its length. Turn the factory scored $\frac{3}{4}$" edges out. Press these edges firmly against the top of the duct, facing the takeoff, and staple the wide side to the joist (Fig. 1). Space between the joists is limited, so an electric stapler works best. I use a carpet stapler with 6 mm crown by 16 mm leg staples (about $\frac{1}{4}$" crown by $\frac{5}{8}$" leg).

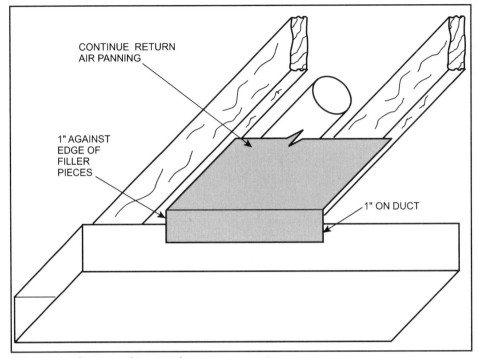

Fig. 2: 2" edge to seal gap and continue panning

For the return air panning on either side of the main supply duct, turn a 2" lip on a piece of panning and press it against the side of the duct (Fig. 2). The panning material has a "memory." Therefore, when the 2" lip is bent to 90° it tends to straighten out. This helps hold it tight against the duct. The top one inch of the 2" turn seals against the ends of the stapled filler pieces and the bottom one inch seals against the side of the duct (Fig. 2). I seal the joint with silver tape to ensure there are no leaks.

To cut panning squarely, I use an aluminum framing square and utility knife. The 2" side blade of the square can also be used as a guide to score for the 2" bend. Use the edge of a dull straight blade screwdriver for scoring so as not to cut the surface of the material. As a guide to score 1" wide lips, I use the 16" long blade from a combination square.

Fig. 3: Vertical header with round hole for branch duct

To make the header where the round branch duct exits the return air space (Fig. 3), the precut Thermo-pan headers must be cut to fit vertically. Precut headers are longer in height than the depth of the joists, so you must re-score the header to the exact depth of the joist to make a vertical fit (Fig. 4). If the header is vertical (not at a slant), you can cut a round hole for it, not the oval hole you would have to make if the header were slanted. (For a normal header with no opening, the header is installed at a slant as explained in Tip 15, Return Air Panning.)

```
                    JOIST
   HEADER
```

Fig. 4: Re-score header so that it can be installed vertically

To make a snug fitting hole in the header for the round branch duct, I mark the circle with a pair of 10" steel point dividers. I score the surface of the header from both sides with the steel points and then finish with a sharp utility knife. With a little practice, this can be done quickly. Follow the scored line with your eye—your hand knows where your eye is looking.

TAKEOFFS AND CONNECTIONS

Tip 19 — INSTALLING TRANSVERSE JOINTS

Getting the transverse joints together on wide duct by yourself can be a bit tricky.

I have my nail-and-chain hanging method of supporting the opposite end while I put the duct together (See Tip 29, "Temporary Hangers"). With duct 18" or less, it is usually fairly easy to start it in the S cleat on one side and swing it into place. However, wide duct tends to sag in the middle, so it is hard to get the top lip into the S cleat. And in tight places where you can't swing much from side to side, you have to bring the duct in straight, so it is hard to get the top lip into the S cleat.

In this situation I drive two short pieces of drive cleat material into the top S cleat (Fig. 1)—one in the middle of the duct and one about two inches in from the side opposite

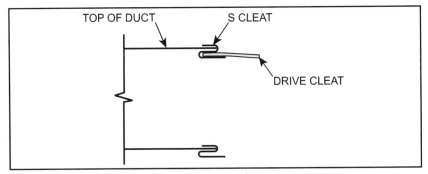

Fig. 1: Drive pieces of drive cleat into S cleat

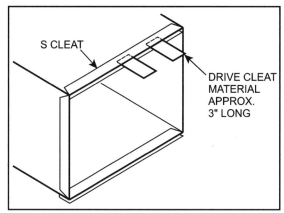

Fig. 2: Drive cleat pieces placed in the middle and on one side

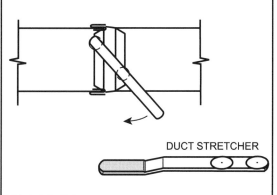

Fig. 3: Use a duct stretcher to bring two pieces of duct together while you start the drive cleat

the side I am working from (Fig. 2). I put a slight downward bend on the drive cleat.

Maneuver the top lip of the duct to rest on top of the pieces of drive cleat material. Start the duct into the top and bottom S cleat on the side you are working from. Usually you can bring the two sections of duct together enough to start a drive cleat with just your hands. If not, use a **duct stretcher** tool to bring the sections together (Fig. 3). I carry two duct stretchers with the wheels on opposite sides, so that I don't have to stop and change the wheels from one side of the offset handle to the other.

With a drive started on one side, carefully swing the duct into the S cleats and start the drive on the other side. Install hangers on the other end of the duct (where the nail-and-chain hanger method has been temporarily holding it at approximately the correct level) and then finish the S and drive transverse joint. The pieces of drive cleat material are left in place.

If the space you are working in is so tight that the duct cannot be swung to the side at all, use three pieces of drive cleat material driven into the top S (Fig. 4). Then it is possible to rest the top lip of the duct on these pieces while you start the duct into the bottom S. You can then go to the end of the duct and by carefully wiggling and raising at the same time, get it slid into the S cleats.

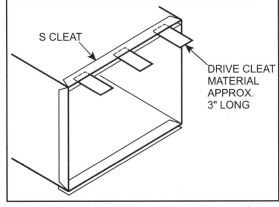

Fig. 4: For tight spaces, use three pieces of drive cleat

Tip **20**

CONNECTING BOOTS AND TAKEOFFS

A piece of round **connector duct** must connect a takeoff from the supply duct to the register boot (Fig 1). Making the connector fit properly can be difficult. Consider these typical dimensions (Fig. 1):

❑ **Supply air ducts** are installed one inch below the bottoms of floor joists.

❑ A standard 6" **top takeoff** from the supply duct fits into the 2 x 10 (actually 1½" x 9¼") joist bay, and it rises 1½" above the supply duct.

❑ A standard **register boot** (4 × 10 × 6) has about a 2" long throat where it attaches to the ¾" subfloor. So the 6" round **connector duct** has to rise about 1½" from the branch takeoff to the register boot opening.

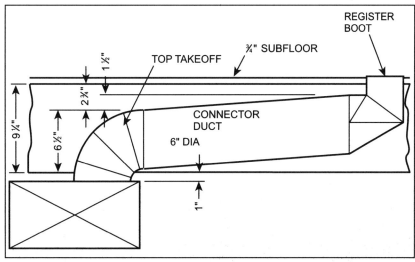

Fig. 1: Typical dimensions for connecting a 6" top takeoff to a register boot

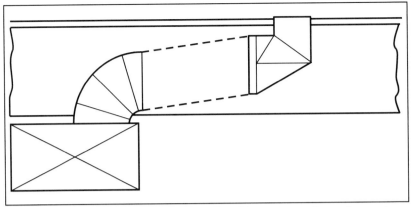

Fig. 2: If the distance between takeoff and boot is too short, the angle may be too sharp for a connector duct

For other conditions and other diameters, the rise will vary.

If the connector duct has enough length, the degree of slope of the round duct does not present a problem for connecting the takeoff to the register boot. However, if the distance is short, the angle of the connector duct at these connections becomes too steep (Fig. 2). I solve this problem in one of three ways:

❑ If there is enough room between the takeoff and the register boot, I offset an adjustable elbow by turning the center joint (Fig. 3).

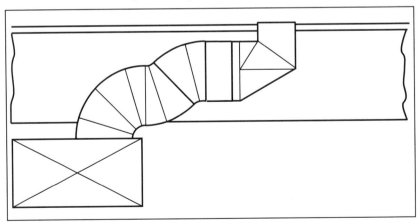

Fig. 3: Using a adjustable elbow as a connector

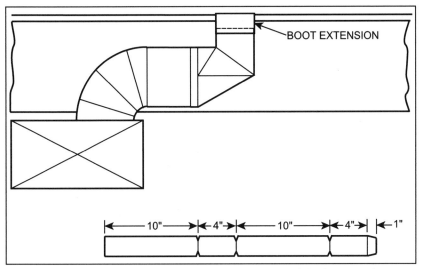

Fig. 4: Make an extension for the rectangular end of the boot so that there is no rise for the connector duct

❑ If there isn't enough room for the offset elbow, I make an extension for the rectangular end of the boot (Fig. 4). This extension can be laid out on one piece of metal and folded up right on the job (Fig. 4). Attach the extension to the boot with S cleats and secure with silver tape.

❑ A third way is to use a short piece of class 1 uninsulated flexible duct between the takeoff and the register boot. If the hole for the register is too close to the duct to allow for the top takeoff to be installed on top of the duct (Fig. 5A), I install it on the side of the duct and elbow up and over the duct (Fig. 5B).

I have had jobs where the register hole was cut immediately above the duct. In this situation I make a rectangular sleeve the size of the register opening and attach it to the top of the duct with S cleats (Fig. 6).

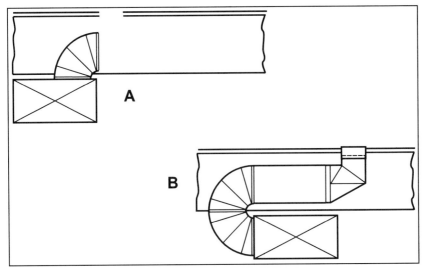

Fig. 5: Install takeoff to side of duct and elbow up to the connector duct

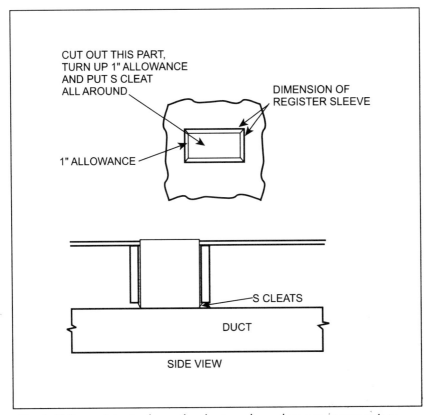

Fig. 6: If the register is above the duct, make a sleeve to connect it to the duct

Tip 21  *TAP-IN CONNECTIONS*

Fig. 1: Offset tap-in plenum takeoff

Probably one of the first fittings you encountered as you began your job of installing residential ductwork was the **tap-in plenum takeoff** (Fig. 1). Perhaps your boss called it a **starting collar** (either straight or offset) or simply a **tap-in**. The tap-in fitting works very well and the offset takeoff (one with a larger opening on the tap-in side and a 45° slope on the throat) is very efficient.

A tap-in is held in place by tapping over the $\frac{3}{4}$" wide tabs. Because of the $\frac{3}{4}$" flange, the hole for this tap-in should be at least $\frac{3}{4}$" below the larger duct it is connected to (Fig. 2).

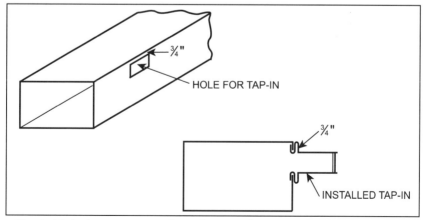

Fig. 2: Hole for tap-in must be at least $\frac{3}{4}$" from top of main duct

Tap-in Flush with Larger Duct

Many times the top of the tap-in needs to be flush with the top of the larger duct, so there is no room for the $\frac{3}{4}$" allowance. I use my hand tongs to turn the top edge of the tap-in into an S (Fig. 3). This S slides over the top edge of the large duct. The other three sides of the tap-in are installed in the usual way and they hold the S in place.

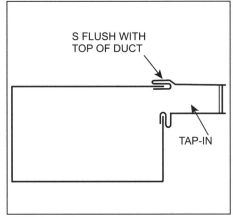

Fig. 3: Tap-in edge formed into an S for a flush fitting

Some shops use a **tap-in with a shoulder** (Fig. 4). With this style, the top of the tap-in can be installed flush with the top of the larger duct without any changes.

The tap-in fitting works well, but it has to be made in the shop or purchased commercially.

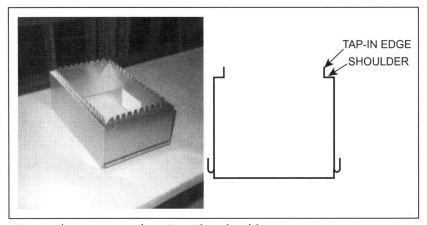

Fig. 4: Alternate type of tap-in with a shoulder

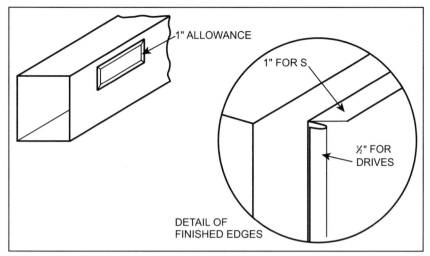

Fig. 5: Tap-in using S and drives can be field-made

Field-made Tap-in

Many years ago I came across a tap-in method on another person's ductwork installation. I remember thinking, this makes a good-looking joint and can be made in the field. It uses S & drives and is laid out right on the duct you are tapping into (Fig. 5). When you cut the hole for the tap-in, allow 1" all around. On the short sides of the hole, bend $\frac{1}{2}$" for drive clips. Then bend all four allowances out 90°. This gives you the edges for an S & drive connection. Connect the duct directly to these.

Of course, the straight tap opening is less efficient than the offset style, but it can be made anywhere a tap is needed. It can be made quickly and neatly with a little practice. I have even made it across an existing transverse joint, either on the S or the drive side as required.

Tap-In in Place of Transition Fitting

When a change in duct size is needed, I have the shop send out a transition fitting if I have the room and the time. However, I sometimes use a tap-in connection in place of a transition fitting. The tap in Fig. 6 is made in the end cap of the larger duct.

A word of caution—abrupt changes in size are less efficient than sloped transition fittings. Be sure you can tolerate the extra pressure drop. It has been my experience that in residential work, it is seldom a problem.

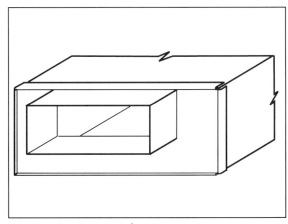

Fig. 6: Tap-in on end cap

Tip 22

FASTENING REGISTER BOOTS IN WOOD FLOORS

I usually fasten register boots in wood floors by nailing into the edge of the flooring material, which is generally OSB (oriented strand board) or plywood. I hold the boot flush with the top surface of the floor while nailing it into the opening.

On most of my install jobs, the register boot openings have already been cut by the rough-in crew. All too often the holes are a little too small to allow the boot to be installed easily, and trimming out every hole is time-consuming.

First I make sure the hole is big enough for the boot. Then I fold in the ends of the boot (Fig. 1). It is now easy to get the boot in the hole, and when I go upstairs to nail it in, the folds pop out with a couple of hammer taps.

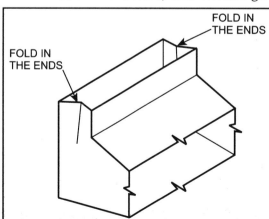

Sometimes, usually for space concerns, I let a portion of the boot stand above the top of the floor and bend the excess down onto the surface of the subfloor. Since it will be

Fig. 1: Make the boot fit a tight hole by folding in the ends

54

covered with carpet or other material, this is not a problem.

Occasionally stacks of drywall cover one or two register openings, preventing me from nailing in the boots. In order to finish the job without a return trip, I turn out a 1" flange on the boot and screw it into place against the bottom surface of the floor. Be sure to use screws that won't penetrate the top surface of the floor.

As an alternate, I sometimes turn out a $\frac{3}{4}$" flange on the short sides of the boot and let the long sides protrude into the register opening in the floor.

Installing at an Angle

The same flange technique can be used to modify a boot so it can be installed at an angle. This could be used to offset the boot far enough to miss some obstruction such as a plumbing pipe. Cut the top at an angle (Fig. 2) and turn 1" flanges out on all sides of the boot. The boot can now be installed at an angle. Screw through the flange to the bottom of the floor.

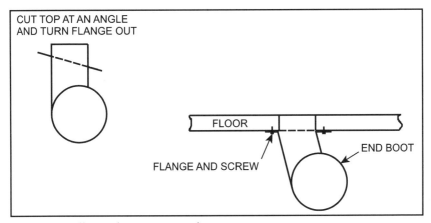

CUT TOP AT AN ANGLE AND TURN FLANGE OUT

FLOOR

END BOOT

FLANGE AND SCREW

Fig. 2: Installing a boot at an angle

Installing to an Angled Register

Quite often I have to install a supply air run where the register hole has been cut at an angle in the joist bay so that it runs parallel to the wall of a bay or bow window wall Fig. 3). In my opinion, this can easily be avoided in most cases, but in our area the builders seem to insist on it. So, since this is a book of installation tips and not one on design, I'll explain how I handle this installation problem.

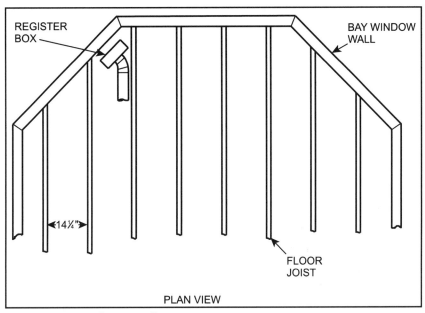

Fig. 3: Bay window installation

The 14¼" joist space isn't big enough for a 90° boot installed at an angle plus an adjustable ell added to bring the pipe run back parallel to the joist. For this kind of run, the company I install for fabricates a register box and a collar (Fig. 4). The collar is sent loose to be tapped on site. To save even more space in the joist run, I usually do not use the collar. I connect the adjustable elbow directly to the register box. Using my duct hole cutter, I make a neat close-fitting hole in the register box, leaving two tabs to turn out for zip screws (Fig. 5). Then I insert the elbow into the hole so that it extends into the box about ¾". I zip screw through the tab to secure the elbow and usually caulk the joint with silicone sealer. When the silicone has set up, it adds a lot of strength to the joint, besides making it leak free. An alternate method is to use a dovetail seam and silicone caulk it, but this takes longer to do.

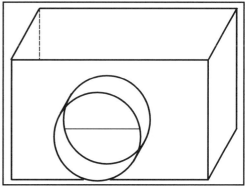

Fig. 4: Register boot and collar

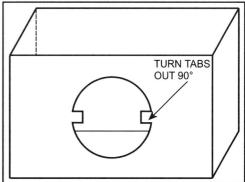

Fig. 5: Hole with screw tabs

Another place where a made-up register box and collar are used as a boot is where a plumbing pipe is in the joist space that must be used (Fig. 6).

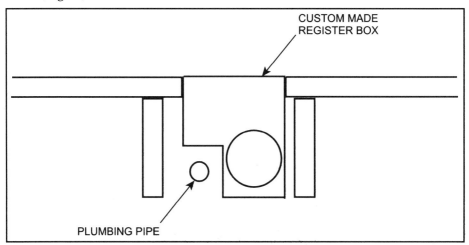

Fig. 6: Register box and collar used as a boot

FIELD MODIFYING DUCT

Tip **23**

FIELD MODIFYING FITTINGS AND DUCT

Field modifying fittings and duct can save time and money. If you install residential ductwork on a performance basis (X number of dollars for the job) as I do, it is sometimes a real benefit.

You have to know how fittings are made before you can alter them. If you learned sheet metal pattern drafting the old-fashioned way at the layout bench, you're all set. However, if you've always worked at a shop with modern computerized layout machines, you may be at a disadvantage when it comes to modifying fittings in the field. In that case, a thorough reading of the book *Layout for Duct Fittings,* in this series, *Indoor Environment Technician's Library,* would be very helpful.

Shortening a Fitting

On a recent job I had a duct run go from 20 x 10 to 16 x 10, but the shop mistakenly sent out a 20 x 10 to 14 x 10 transition fitting. Rather than order a new fitting (which would have caused a delay for me and extra time and expense for the shop) I field-modified the fitting. I decided I could cut off the fitting at the point where the side measured 16" (Fig. 1). This made a shorter fitting, but I could make other adjustments so that the short fitting was still acceptable. However, in other situations, a shorter fitting would not be acceptable.

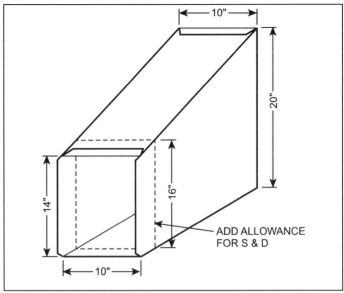

Fig. 1: Cut off the fitting so that the side measures 16"

I prefer to disassemble the fitting before I cut it off. I think it is easier to make the modifications that way, and that it makes a more finished product.

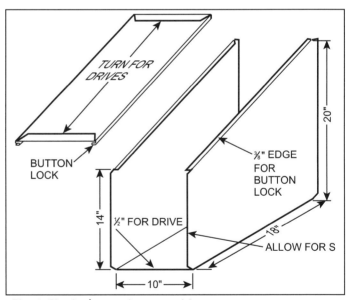

Fig. 2: Typical two-piece transition

Typically, when there is a change in only one dimension, the fitting is made in two pieces (Fig. 2). While a button lock joint won't come apart directly, you can slide it apart along its length by tapping on the end of the sloped side

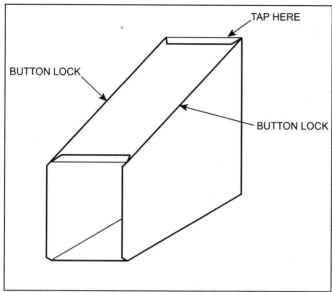

TAP HERE

BUTTON LOCK

BUTTON LOCK

Fig. 3: Tap on side to slide button lock apart

(Fig. 3). It's a good idea to hold a board against the metal edge and tap on this to avoid denting the metal. A Pittsburgh lock can be disassembled fairly easily by opening the lock with a putty knife or other tool.

After the fitting is disassembled, cut the pieces to the proper dimensions. Be sure to leave enough material for the S & drive connection. Before you reassemble the fitting, the multiple thickness of the button lock or the Pittsburgh lock has to be cut back 1", flattened, and notched for the S & drives. Open up the lock and cut the double thickness back an inch so that the last inch can be flattened and notched for S & drives.

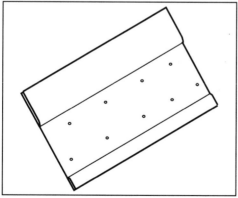

I use a folding tool (Fig. 4) to turn the edges for the drive cleats and a hand seamer (hand tongs) to flatten it. In some cases I also use a hand seamer to turn the edge.

Fig. 4: Use a folding tool to turn edges for drive cleats

Cutting Off a Fitting

To modify a fitting that can't be taken apart readily—for example, to shorten a large supply air fitting at the air handling equipment—I cut it off with straight snips or aviation snips. You can use bulldog snips to cut the many folds at the corners. However, the cuts at the corners are rather difficult to make and it is hard on the snips. Usually I make the corner cuts with a cutting wheel in my 4½" grinder and finish the cuts with straight snips. Another way is to cut the corners with a hacksaw or a metal cutting blade in a reciprocating saw and finish the side cuts with straight snips.

Cutting Straight Duct

Cutting straight pieces of duct in the field is easy. I lay a half section on my temporary work bench (a hollow core door on a pair of sawhorses) with the short side hanging down off the side of my bench. I mark the length with a felt tip pen and a framing T or framing square, allowing for S and drives. I then cut the folds of the button lock with bulldog aviation snips and then cut up the rest of the way on the short side with straight snips. I cut the long side from the other side of the bench. If the drop-off is less than 12", I cut to get rid of the short side waste and then finish the cut on the long side from the same side of the bench. I cut away the folds of the lock, and notch for S & drives.

Making Narrow Duct from Wide Duct

Making a piece of narrower duct from a piece of wider two-piece duct is easy, especially if it is short (36" or less).

For example, you need 24" of 14 x 8 duct, but the only pieces on the job are 16 x 8. Cut the 16 x 8 pieces to 14" wide plus the $\frac{3}{8}$" allowance for the button lock edge. Use a folding tool to turn the $\frac{3}{8}$" edge (or use hand tongs). Add buttons to the edge with a button lock (snap lock) punch and assemble.

KNOW THE THREE PRESSURES IN DUCT

Leo's Tip

Whenever air flows in a duct, there are three air pressures:

- ❑ **Velocity pressure (VP)**

  It requires pressure to push a car. It also requires pressure to push air through a duct. The fan creates this pressure. The fan moves air and creates velocity pressure. The greater the velocity (speed) of the air, the higher the velocity pressure. When you feel the wind on your face, you are feeling the velocity pressure of the wind.

- ❑ **Static pressure (SP)**

  Static means *not moving*. A balloon stays inflated because the pressure is pressing in all directions even though the air is not moving. Static pressure in a duct also presses in all directions whether the air is moving or not.

- ❑ **Total pressure (TP)**

  Total pressure in a duct is the sum of VP and SP:

  $$TP = VP + SP$$

Tip 24  ANOTHER FIELD MODIFIED FITTING

The photo in Fig. 1 shows a 14 x 10 elbow from a yet-to-be-installed 14 x 10 return air trunk duct, going into a 16 x 10 return air trunk duct. It was supposed to be a 16 x 10 to 14 x 10 reducing elbow. Rather than have the shop make and send out a new elbow, I used a field made filler piece (Fig. 2).

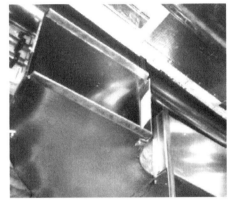

Fig. 1: A 14 x 10 elbow on a 16 x 10 return air duct

NOTE: This is not recommended as a general practice. Abrupt changes in size are very inefficient and result in higher pressure losses.

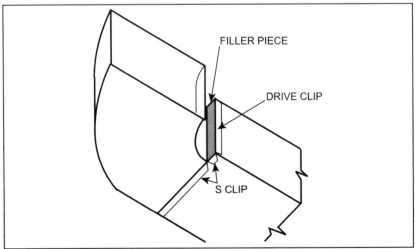

Fig. 2: Filler piece

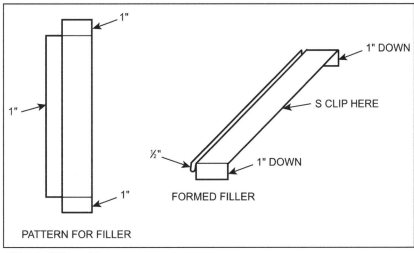

1"

1" DOWN

S CLIP HERE

½"

1" DOWN

FORMED FILLER

1"

1"

PATTERN FOR FILLER

Fig. 3: Filler piece

However, on this particular job it was not a critical issue. I'm describing it here only to show how I made the filler pieces.

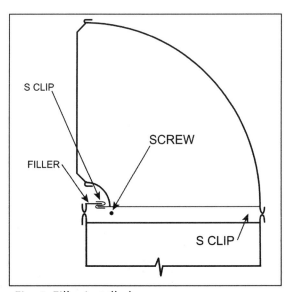

S CLIP

SCREW

FILLER

S CLIP

Fig. 4: Filler installed

Lay out the filler to the dimension needed plus 1" allowance on three sides (Fig. 3). I use my folding tool to make the 1" 90° bends and the fold for the drive cleat.

Attach the filler to the elbow with an S cleat as shown in Fig. 4. To keep the ell from swinging out of place, I put a zip screw through the S cleat of the transverse joint (Fig. 4). You should pre-drill for this screw, as there are several layers of metal to go through.

Tip

CUTTING A DOGLEG OFFSET

A **dogleg offset** (Fig. 1) is made from a straight piece of duct. Here are warnings about a dogleg offset:

1. **It is not acceptable** in some areas or on some jobs.

2. Even if it is acceptable, use it **only when there is no other way to do the job**. It creates a greater resistance to airflow than a radius throat elbow or an S offset. This means that it reduces the quantity of airflow through the duct.

3. Unless the joints are carefully made, there will be excessive air leakage. This means wasted energy. All the joints must be sealed with an acceptable sealer.

4. A dogleg offset should never be used for an offset of more than 15°. The angle-cut on the offset will be longer than the square end of the duct, and the greater the offset, the larger the difference in length of the two ends. If there is too much difference, you

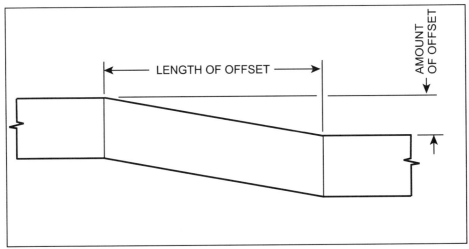

Fig. 1: Dogleg offset

will have a leakage problem. A 15° offset has $3\frac{1}{4}$"
of offset for every foot (12") of offset length.

To make a dogleg offset, you need to find the angle of the
cut to be made on the offset piece. Start with a square
corner. If you are using a door for a workbench (See Tip 1),
you can use the long edge of the door as a base and one
corner of the door as the square corner. The following
explanation is based on using the square corner of the door,
but you can use any square corner.

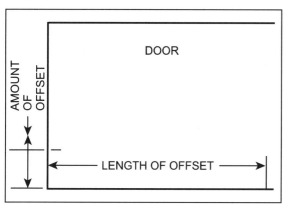

Fig. 2: Mark offset on door

Mark the **amount of
offset** at the end of the
door (Fig. 2). Measure the
length of the offset on the
long edge of the door.
Use a framing square to
mark a line perpendicular
to the long edge to show
the **length of offset**
(Fig. 2). Then lay the duct
right on the bench at the
required offset and length and transfer the slant cut lines to
the duct (Fig. 3).

Before cutting, be sure to add laps in the direction of the
airflow and add notches.

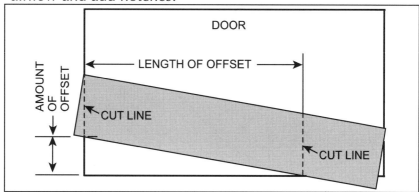

Fig. 3: Lay duct on offset lines and mark cut

USING DRIVE CLEATS

Tip **26**

PREPARING DRIVE CLEATS

Many shops produce properly notched drive cleats in standard lengths (8", 10", and 12"). These are already notched for easy starting (Fig. 1). I also carry random lengths such as 16", 24", and 48". These can be cut to the required length and notched on the job. To notch them, I hold the end of the cleat against my bench and open the end with a screwdriver, first one side and then the other, with a rolling motion. (The drive and the screwdriver both point away from me and into the bench.) Then I finish the V notch with aviation snips. Cut the sides that are the same at one time before changing snips and cutting the other sides.

Fig. 1: Notched end of drive cleat

Be safe when clipping drive cleats. After the top is hammered over the top of the duct, I cut the bottom off approximately 1" long and clip the corners. When clipping the corners with aviation snips, protect your face and eyes. I hold my hand in front of the snips when they are positioned on the side that will throw the cut-off toward me.

To fold the bottom 1" of the clip around the duct, I usually start the bend with my hand tongs and then finish with a hammer. There is less chance of twisting the duct that way.

Leo's Tip

UNDERSTANDING RELATIVE HUMIDITY

Humidity is the amount of moisture in the air. Air conditioning is concerned with the relative humidity of the air because it is an important part of comfort. **Relative humidity (RH)** is the percent of moisture in the air as compared to 100% of the moisture that air at that temperature can hold:

❑ An air measurement of 70°F, 50% RH means that the air contains 50% of the moisture that the air is capable of holding at 70°F.

The amount of moisture that air can hold varies with the temperature. The warmer the air is, the more moisture it can hold. For example, suppose that air at 60°F has an RH of 50%. If the temperature rises to 80°F and the moisture content does not change, the RH will decrease to 27%. The relative humidity has gone down, but the amount of moisture in the air remains the same.

Relative humidity is as important as temperature in creating comfort conditions in air conditioning. Generally, people feel more comfortable in a range of 30% to 60% RH.

Tip 27

DRIVE CLEAT AS DAMPER HANDLE EXTENSION

I had a situation where a trunk duct volume damper handle was inaccessible between closely spaced adjacent ducts. So I used a piece of drive cleat material to make an extension that hung down below the bottom of the duct (Fig. 1).

I fastened the cleat to the damper handle with a nut and bolt. Leave the nut loose enough so the drive cleat pivots on the handle. Be sure to smash the threads on the bolt so that the nut cannot work off.

Mark the drive cleat with a magic marker (Fig. 1) to indicate the open and closed directions.

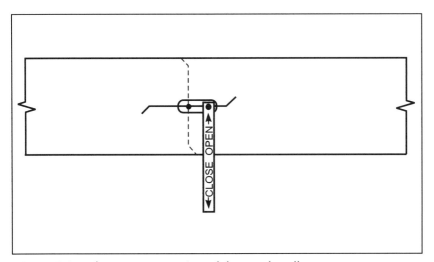

Fig. 1: Drive cleat as an extension of damper handle

Tip 28

FIELD FABRICATING A WIDE DRIVE CLEAT

You will, no doubt, occasionally have a situation where one side of an S & drive transverse joint can't be brought together close enough for a standard drive cleat to be used.

For example, I often set the furnace and install the ductwork in the basement of two-story houses after the riser to the second floor has already been installed at the rough-in stage. This riser extends down through the floor to a point approximately one inch below the floor joists. The bottom of the riser is not always level—but at this point, it is very rigid and not easily moved. If the basement floor is parallel to the floor joists, one side of the transverse joint will be more open than its opposite side (Fig. 1).

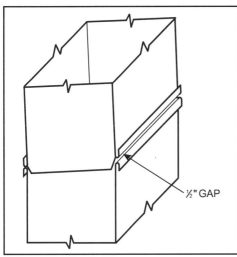

½" GAP

Fig. 1: Gap between drive bends

There are usually at least two transverse joints in the connection between the air handler and the riser, so if the unlevel condition is not too severe, the normal play in the transverse joints will allow the connection to be made. If there is a canvas connection at the unit, the difference can be made up there.

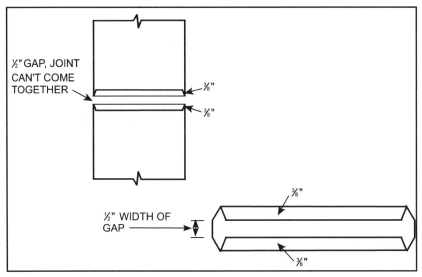

Fig. 2: Special drive clip

Sometimes though, there is no play. In this case I field fabricate a wide drive cleat made for the wide gap (Fig. 2). In this case, the gap is $\frac{1}{2}$".

The width needed for the drive cleat strip is the width of the gap plus $1\frac{3}{4}$", which includes (Fig. 3):

$$\frac{3}{8}" + \frac{3}{8}" + \frac{3}{8}" + \frac{3}{8}" = 1\frac{1}{2}"$$

$$\frac{1}{16}" \text{ for bends } + \frac{1}{16}" \text{ for play} = \frac{1}{4}"$$
$$\overline{1\frac{3}{4}"}$$

For the $\frac{1}{2}$" gap in Fig. 2, the strip would be $2\frac{1}{4}$" wide ($\frac{1}{2}$" gap + $1\frac{3}{4}$").

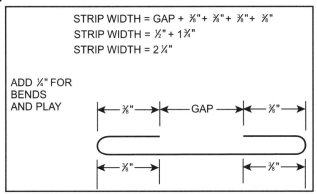

Fig. 3: Width of strip for special drive clip

HANGERS AND SUPPORTS

Tip 29

FURNACE CHAIN AS TEMPORARY HANGER

To hang lengths of duct by myself, I often use two 8 foot lengths of **furnace chain** (so called because it was once used to remotely open flue and draft dampers on wood-fired or coal-fired furnaces). I'm sure you will find many ways of using this chain and nail method as a temporary hanger.

I cut the heads off 3d galvanized nails that I carry in my tool pouch for nailing in register boots. I drive these nails into the joists at the required locations and hook the furnace chain on them through the links of the chain. There are many small links in this type of chain allowing for fine adjustments. I make a loose loop with the chain (Fig. 1) and use this to cradle one or both ends of the duct while I make the necessary connections and install the permanent hangers.

Fig. 1: Furnace chain ready to use as a temporary hanger

The furnace chain and nails work great when there is wood above the point where I need the hanger. However, sometimes there is metal above—for example, a larger rectangular branch duct or a steel beam.

For this I use a strong magnet and a cable such as a Kwiktwist tie or a large Ty-Rap (Fig. 2). After the run is in place, I secure it with permanent Ty-Raps or metal straps and then remove the temporary hanger.

The set-up in the photo is just to show the magnet and Kwiktwist tie—it is not an actual installation.

Fig. 2: Magnet and cable as temporary hanger

Leo's Tip KEEP ENOUGH VENTILATION

Be sure to provide the amount of ventilation air set by codes. Too little ventilation can cause health problems:

- ❑ Carbon monoxide (CO) is a deadly gas that is a result of incomplete combustion. It is produced by propane, natural gas, or kerosene heaters that are faulty or unvented.
- ❑ Carbon dioxide (CO_2) is exhaled as we breathe. It can build up in crowded areas that are not properly ventilated. CO_2 itself is not hazardous, but as it increases, the oxygen level decreases. Low oxygen levels are dangerous.
- ❑ Many cleaning solvents, paints, colognes, adhesives, and other products give off hazardous or unpleasant fumes.

Tip 30

L-SHAPED JIG AS TEMPORARY HANGER

Another method for hanging duct solo is fast and easy. It works with smaller duct—up to 20" wide. I use a permanent duct hanger and an **L-shaped jig** (Fig. 1) made from random lengths of drive stock material. To make the L-shaped jig:

❑ Turn the short leg up 90°.

❑ Use two pairs of hand tongs to make a twist in the short leg so it can lie flat against the side of the floor joist.

❑ Drive a #8 x 1" zip screw through the end of the long leg. This screw is used as a temporary connection to the permanent hanger.

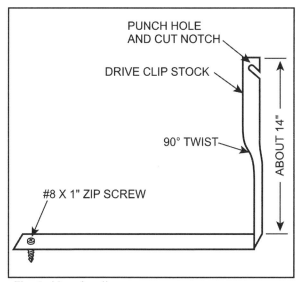

PUNCH HOLE AND CUT NOTCH

DRIVE CLIP STOCK

90° TWIST

ABOUT 14"

#8 X 1" ZIP SCREW

Fig. 1: Hanging jig

❑ Punch a hole and cut a slot to it on the short leg. This is used to engage a 3d nail in the side of the joist.

I carry two sizes of this jig—one bottom leg is 18" long and the other is 24" long. But if you forget them or

74

lose them, they can be
made on the job in just
minutes.

To install the duct, first
prepare and install a
**permanent duct
hanger** for one side of
the duct (Fig. 2). On

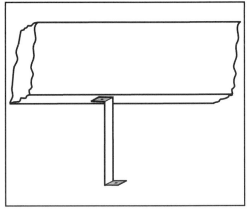

Fig. 2: Install permanent hanger

supply air duct there is
an inch clearance
between the duct and
the joist, so I screw the
hanger up tight to the
joist (I use 1" zip
screws). However, on
return air duct I usually
leave the hanger screw
loose until I have the
duct up and the
transverse joint made
before I run it up tight
to the joist. This gives
me a little extra room
to move the duct.

*Fig. 3: Jig and permanent hanger in
position*

Figure 3 shows the jig
and the permanent duct hanger in position. You might use
them this way and slide the duct through if the piece of duct
is small enough and short enough. However, I usually set it
up like this just to locate and install the 3d nail into the
joist.

To hang the duct if you don't slide it through, unhook the
jig from the 3d nail and let it hang down with the 1" zip

screw through the hole in the permanent hanger. (It won't slip out.) Raise the duct and rest the end in the S sides of the previous piece. Hold it there with one hand, and swing the L-shaped jig up and hook it on the 3d nail with the other hand. You don't have to be in a position to see the nail—just slide the edge along the nail and it will fall into the downward-sloping slot.

Now you can make up the S & drive transverse joint. It is easy to do because the jig holds the duct at the proper level, and it allows some swinging motion because it is wider than the duct.

When the joints are made up, replace the L-shaped jig with a permanent duct hanger. If necessary, tighten the screw on the first permanent hanger.

| *Leo's* | V-BELT DRIVE SYSTEM |
| *Tip* | A V-belt drive system consists of a **drive sheave** |

A V-belt drive system consists of a **drive sheave** (motor sheave, often called the **drive**), a **driven sheave** (fan sheave), and a **V-belt**. The word **sheave** is pronounced **shiv** (rhymes with give).

Sheave diameters are stated as **pitch diameter** (**PD**) or **datum diameter** (**DD**). The PD or DD is the working diameter of the sheave, and is a little less than the outside diameter (OD). PD or DD is the diameter of the sheave that makes contact with the point of the V-belt that neither contracts or expands (the pitch length of the belt). It is important because it is the diameter that determines the speed ratio between the motor and the fan.

Pitch diameter (PD) used to be the only term used. Now the term datum diameter (DD) is used for sheaves for belt sizes A, B, C and D. The term pitch diameter is still commonly used in the industry. However, in catalogs, you will see datum diameter used.

Tip **31**

DUCT STRETCHER AS TEMPORARY HANGER

DUCT STRETCHER

A four-foot section of 20 x 16 return air drop duct is rather heavy and awkward for one person to install without some help. I get my **duct stretcher** tool to help me. It makes an excellent temporary hanger (Fig. 1).

Hang the duct stretcher in the center of the drive turn of the previous piece. Then, facing the wheel side of the duct stretcher, hang your drop section on the bottom wheel.

Now you can make up the connection on your side (the side opposite the duct stretcher). Then go to the other side and use the duct stretcher in the usual way to bring the sections together and install the drive cleat.

It's a good idea to carry two duct stretchers when you work alone.

Fig. 1: Duct stretcher tool used as temporary support for return air drop duct

Tip 32

ROUND DUCT HANGERS

USING TY-RAPS

Round duct installed perpendicular to joists requires a hanger. For this I usually use 36" long nylon **Ty-Raps** (Fig. 1). (Check your local codes. Some areas require metal straps.)

For a temporary hanger to position and align the duct, I use my handy nail and furnace chain method (See Tip 29). Then with the duct held in place, I zip screw the joints and install the Ty-Rap hangers.

To install the Ty-Raps, I drive an electrician's wire and cable staple partially into the joist centered above the duct

Fig. 1: Ty-Rap used as round duct hanger

(Fig. 2). Then I thread a Ty-Rap through the staple, loop it around the duct, and secure it. When the duct is permanently installed, I remove the furnace chain clamps.

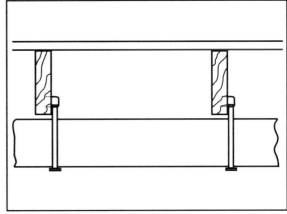

Fig. 2: Electrician's wire and cable staple driven partially into joist

Using Jack Chain

To hang flue pipe, which would get too hot for nylon Ty-Raps, I might use **jack chain**, a light duty small link chain. (Check your local codes to see if this is acceptable.)

I cut the heads off two 3d galvanized nails, always available in my tool pouch, and drive them into the side of the joist above the flue pipe. Hook the jack chain on these nails. Getting the flue pipe into the proper position is easy because of the adjustment provided by the links in the chain.

When the pipe is in the right place, I bend the nails over and cut off the excess chain.

Tip 33

HANGERS FOR ROUND DUCT ATTACHED TO RECTANGULAR DUCT

Tip 32 described how I use nylon Ty-Raps for round duct hangers. When there are wood joists above the duct, I use an electrician's wire and cable staple to loop the Ty-Rap through.

Recently I had a 6" round duct passing under a wide rectangular duct. The round duct needed to be secured to the rectangular duct. I used a strap made of a 1" wide strip of metal with a hole in each end for this (Fig. 1).

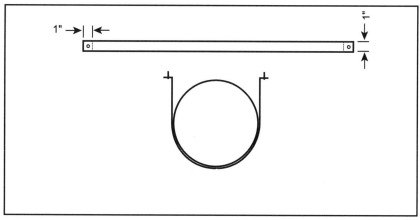

Fig. 1: Use a metal strap to secure round duct to a rectangular duct

80

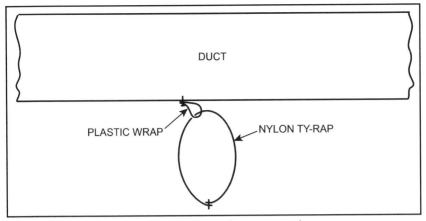

Fig. 2: Use a short plastic strap to attach to Ty-Rap hanger

I have also used a short plastic strap zip screwed to the duct to loop a Ty-Rap through (Fig. 2). (Check your local code to see if this is allowed.)

If possible, fasten hangers near the corner edges of the rectangular duct. If you fasten near the middle, the metal of the rectangular duct will sag.

Leo's Tip — **USE THE RIGHT V-BELT**

Installing the wrong V-belt can damage equipment, reduce belt life, and reduce the transmitted horsepower. Belts should be selected by letter type and length. An identification number (such as 4L-400) is stamped on the outside of the belt.

L belts are **fractional horsepower** belts and are used for residential applications. They are light and flexible to fit around the smaller sheaves.

A, B, C, and **D** belts are used on medium and large fans in commercial and industrial applications. They are designed for higher horsepower and a longer life than fractional horsepower belts.

Tip **34**

JOB-MADE DUCT HANGERS

I often make my duct hangers from drive cleat material. In general, I add 2" to the required length and turn out 1" at top and 1" at the bottom in opposite directions (Fig. 1). I

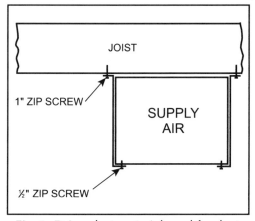

Fig. 1: Drive cleat material used for duct hanger

punch a $\frac{5}{32}$" hole with a Roper Whitney No. 5 hand punch in the 1" turnouts. The holes keep the hanger from twisting when the zip screw bottoms out.

If the duct is close to a wall or some other obstruction, I turn both 1" turnouts the same way (Fig. 2). Of course, in this case you have to install the hanger before hanging the duct because the screw will be above the duct. If the duct is a return air duct hung tight to the joist, I use a flat heat screw into the joist instead of a hex head zip screw (which would interfere with the duct).

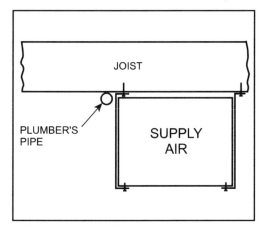

Fig. 2: Turnouts face in the same direction to avoid an obstruction

If the duct runs parallel to the joist, cut a hanger that will reach to the bottom of the subfloor, and screw it into the subfloor. However, remember to use a screw that doesn't penetrate the subfloor. I usually use a ¾" long zip screw. Be careful though—if you "spin out" the screw it will lose its holding power.

Drive cleat material can be used to make any number of hangers or brackets:

❏ With two pairs of hand seamers (tongs), make a twist in the hanger so that it will fasten to a support at an angle to the duct (Fig. 3).

❏ Make an angle piece by bending a drive in the center along its length. This could be used, for example, to support a flue pipe running along the side of a supply air plenum (Fig. 4).

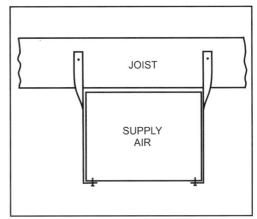

Fig. 3: Use tongs to make a twist in the hanger

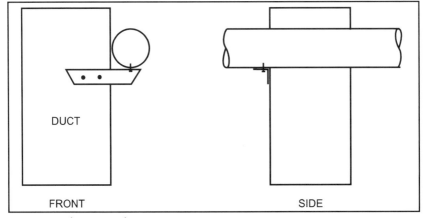

Fig. 4: Make an angle piece to serve as a support

❏ Make brackets (Fig. 5) to support pipes running beside ducts.

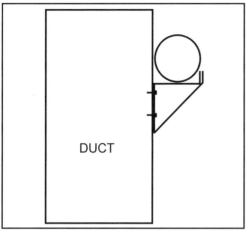

DUCT

Fig. 5: Drive cleat material used to make a bracket

So, as you can see, with some lengths of drive cleat material, hand seamers (tongs), a hand punch, zip screws, and a screw gun you can meet most of your hanger and bracketing needs for the typical residential duct installation—and have a neat workman-like job.

V-BELT HORSEPOWER

Leo's Tip

In addition to cross section and pitch length, V-belts are also rated by the **horsepower** (**Hp**) they will transmit. To determine the horsepower of a belt, refer to the manufacturer's catalog. In general, the Hp rating for a single V-belt should be at least 1.5 times the motor Hp. For multiple belts, the total of the belt Hp ratings should be 1.5 times the motor Hp. The extra capacity is to prevent belt slippage when the motor starts and the drive system must overcome the inertia of the fan wheel. If a belt is rated at less than motor Hp, it will slip at starting—and may slip while running. The belt will also have a shorter life and may damage the motor sheave. If you see a motor sheave that is polished in the V, the belt is probably slipping, perhaps because the Hp rating of the belt is not adequate.

84

Tip **35**

S CLEAT
FOR DUCT
SUPPORT

To support round duct in joist bays, I use S cleat material (Fig. 1). Similar duct supports are also made commercially. However, S cleats are already on the job, and they can be cut to any size. S cleats are 3-fold thick, so are most easily cut with bulldog style aviation snips.

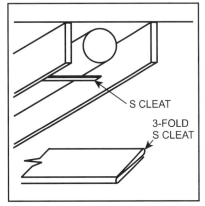

Fig. 1: S cleat used to support round duct

Cut the S cleat material 1" longer than the inside of the joist bay, with the ends cut at a slight angle parallel to each other (Fig. 2). To install, drive the S cleat into the sides of the joist with a twisting/slicing motion (Fig. 3).

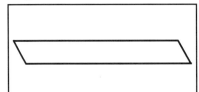

Fig. 2: Cut the ends at an angle

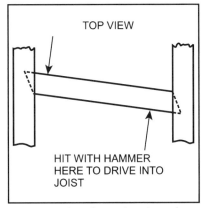

Fig. 3: Drive the points into the joists

Tip 36  *USING BOOT EARS*

I expect most installers use tabs on the sides of boots for fastening them in a joist bay. In my part of the country the tabs are called **boot ears** (Fig. 1), but they are also called **plaster stop**.

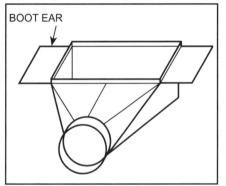

Fig. 1: Boot with boot ears

The company I install for sends out 8 foot pieces that are 5" wide with a standing seam on one edge. These pieces can then be cut crossway to the proper length. I have fashioned boot ears from flat strips of metal by turning a $\frac{1}{2}$" standing seam on one end (Fig. 2) with a hand-held folding tool.

Fig. 2: Strip of metal with $\frac{1}{2}$" standing seam for boot ears

To install the boot ears, slip the $\frac{1}{2}$" standing seam onto the edge of the boot and crimp with a hand-held button lock tool. This makes a secure attachment. If it is needed, I stiffen the long edges of the boot with S cleats.

When 10" wide boots are installed in a 24" OC joist bay, they need more support than a boot ear alone. So I use 26" long drive cleats along with boot ear material.

I fasten the boot ears to the drive cleat and fasten the drive cleat to the joists (Figs. 3 and 4):

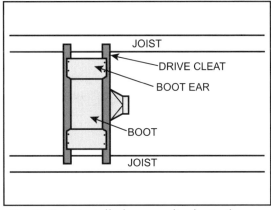

Fig. 3: Boot installed perpendicular to the joists

- ❏ If the long dimension of the boot is **perpendicular to the joists** (Fig. 3), I make the boot ears wider than the boot. I use a hand tool to button-lock the boot ear to the boot, and then button-lock the drive cleat to the wing of the boot ear (Fig. 3).

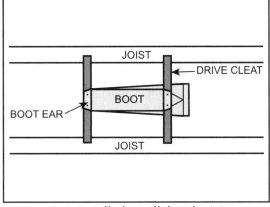

Fig. 4: Boot installed parallel to the joists

- ❏ If the long dimension of the boot is **parallel to the joists** (Fig. 4), I trim the boot ear to the width of the drive cleat and button-lock the drive cleat to the boot ear.

To fasten the drive cleat to the joists, I use a gas-operated framing nailer that is set to drive the nail flush. Using the nailer also allows me to hold the boot assembly in place with one hand while nailing with the other. A screw gun and zip screws work equally well.

Tip 37

SUPPLY AIR DAMPERS

For forty years—first as a plumbing, heating, and electrical contractor and then as a builder doing all my own HVAC work—I installed supply air runs without (for the most part) individual dampers in them, with few customer complaints. I was able to do this by using room-by-room heat loss/heat gain figures and correctly sizing the branch ducts and then using a mix of 4", 5", 6", and 7" round supply air runs.

However, I realize that some codes require dampers on individual runs. The firm that I now install for uses almost exclusively 6" round runs with dampers in each run. I agree that a damper installed immediately following a run takeoff can provide the best control of the air to that run.

But in many of the upper end, two-story houses where I install ductwork, the runs are above finished ceilings. Therefore, dampers at takeoffs are either difficult to reach or inaccessible. To make the dampers accessible and to avoid unsightly damper rod extensions, some firms require that the dampers be installed in the register boot. To do this we install a 6" round damper that can be reached through the register opening for adjusting. The register must be removed to adjust these dampers. Generally this is done only once at the balancing stage of the installation.

Dampers in this location do not have as good air control as dampers at takeoffs. Also they create greater air noise, and disrupt both the air pattern and throw. However, they do have an advantage over dampers that are part of the register. This is because if there are no register dampers, residents are less likely to throw the system out of balance by constantly adjusting dampers.

Leo's Tip

V-BELT LENGTH

V-belt length is given in catalogs in three ways—outside length, pitch length, and nominal length.

- **Outside length**
  Outside length is simply the length of the belt as measured around the outside.

- **Pitch length (PL)**
  Imagine a belt traveling around a sheave, and you can see that the outside portion of the belt has to stretch and the inside portion has to compress as it goes around the curve of the sheave. The pitch length (PL) of a belt is the line somewhere in the belt that neither stretches nor compresses as it travels around the sheaves.

- **Nominal length**
  Nominal means the name given to something. The nominal length of a belt is simply the name given to a certain size belt and is its approximate length. Nominal length is usually a bit less than pitch length. Most belts have the size and nominal length (such as A78) printed on the side.

Compare the nominal length, pitch length, and outside length of these A belt sizes:

A40 (nominal length) 41.3" pitch length 42.2" outside length
A50 (nominal length) 51.3" pitch length 52.2" outside length
A78 (nominal length) 79.3" pitch length 80.2" outside length

Tip 38

BOOT EAR MATERIAL AS FILLER

As mentioned elsewhere, I get my boot ear material in 8-foot pieces—5" wide with a $\frac{1}{2}$" standing fold on one edge (Fig. 1). I make an additional fold on the boot ear material to form an S (Fig. 2).

I use this material to fill in the extra space when I have an evaporator coil that is wider than the furnace I have to fit it to. I fit the S on the $\frac{3}{4}$" edge on the furnace (Fig. 3). When the coil is lowered onto the furnace, it seals against the boot ear material (Fig. 3).

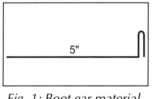

Fig. 1: Boot ear material

Fig. 2: Additional fold on boot ear material

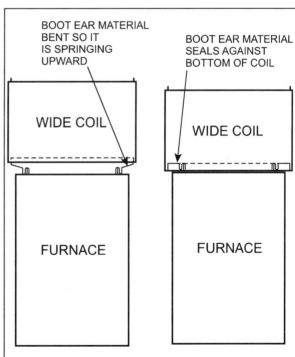

Fig. 3: Using boot ear material to connect a wide coil to a furnace

Tip 39 VENTS FOR GAS FURNACES AND WATER HEATERS

The use of single wall pipe and elbows for flue connectors is allowed by most codes. However, most codes limit how they can be used. **Be sure you know your local code**.

To be safe, I use flexible, double wall connectors for all my installations. These can be ordered in lengths of from one foot to five feet. To meet code they cannot be cut. Most codes approve them for Type B double-wall connectors. Elbows and other fittings can also be ordered.

Be sure you know the category classification of your appliance. Type B vent systems are for Category I appliances. For other categories, consult the manufacturer's instructions.

Know your local code. Keep these things in mind:

❑ Keep runs as vertical as possible. Avoid lateral runs.

❑ Use 45° or 60° degree elbows rather than 90° for less resistance. For the same reason use a wye instead of a tee.

❑ If you must use a vent on the exterior of the building, enclose it in an insulated chase. The vent must be warm to draw properly.

❑ The clearance for a single wall vent is 6" from wood. The clearance for double-wall vents is 1".

Tip **40**

CLEANUP

We aren't required to leave our work area broom clean—but we do have to pick up our metal scrap. To save my back, I pick up my metal scrap with a magnet-on-a-stick. They are available at most home stores.

Leo's Tip

WORK SAFELY ON FANS

Follow safety rules when you work on a fan V-belt drive system:

- ❑ Lock out and tag out. Turn off the circuit breaker and tape it. Inform anyone in the house why it is off.
- ❑ Sometimes a switch is wired wrong and the circuit is still live although the switch is off. Test at the motor with a voltage meter or test light.
- ❑ Let a fan roll to a stop. NEVER try to stop it with your hands.
- ❑ **Never** put your fingers under a V-belt, even if the fan is off. Any movement of the belt can crush your fingers.

Tip 41

TAKEOFFS, BOOTS, AND STACKHEADS

These are some of the standard takeoffs, boots, and stackheads that you can order from the manufacturer.